At least seven feet
parchment that had
vampire was the mo
that Marlowe had even seen. His pale blue hair darkened to the center and rose to a high crest that added another nine inches to his height. His eyes were lensed over and flashed the same blue. As he confronted Marlowe, he swept back his cape in a dramatic gesture which revealed a black vinyl body suit that left his arms bare. There was a stim block strapped to each wrist with lines going to a switchboard of receptors running all the way up to his biceps. A third stim block hung from his neck by a silver chain, its lines going to receptors at his throat. And when he smiled, Marlowe saw a mouthful of gold fangs!

Also by Mick Farren in Sphere Books:

THEIR MASTER'S WAR

EXIT FUNTOPIA

Mick Farren

SPHERE BOOKS LIMITED

A SPHERE BOOK

First published in the United States of America by Ballantine Books 1988

First published in Great Britain by Sphere Books Ltd 1989

Printed and bound in Great Britain by
Richard Clay Ltd, Bungay, Suffolk

Sphere Books Ltd
A Division of
Macdonald & Co. (Publishers) Ltd
66/73 Shoe Lane, London EC4P 4AB
A Member of Maxwell Pergamon Publishing Corporation plc

ONE

MARLOWE LIT A CIGARETTE. IT WAS A ZIMBABWE Pall Mall, smuggled in through Canada. That was the way all cigarettes came in since prohibition. Of course, everyone knew that prohibition was a shuck. Cigarettes had only been outlawed after every tobacco plant in North America had been killed off by the DX virus. The Jamison Act was hardly enforced, and anyone could buy a carton on just about every street corner in the Zone. Marlowe coughed and reached for the autolin inhaler. What the hell? He knew that smoking was a disgusting, dangerous habit, but it was such a crucial part of his persona that there was nothing else he could do. Sam Spade, Mike Hammer—they all smoked. He told himself that smoking couldn't be any worse than breathing the air. The view through the double glazing tended to confirm that idea. The air was swamp-green and sluggish with dirty moisture. The temperature outside had to be in the low nineties, and his elderly air conditioner made moist, grinding noises as it labored to keep the apartment tolerable. The bad greenhouse summer lay on the city like a heavy blanket. On a clear day he could see across the block. Marlowe noticed that there was algae growing between the panes of the double glazing. That shouldn't be happening on the forty-fifth floor, but it was only what could be expected in a building as old and poorly maintained as this one.

The big wall screen was playing "Gilligan's Island." Marlowe didn't know what it was that made him order up antique sitcoms. They weren't even his period. It had to be some bizarre form of self-punishment. He hated "Gilligan's Island." He hated all of them: Gilligan, the Skipper, Thurston and Lovey, Ginger—well, maybe not Ginger. It was hard to hate anyone who looked like Tina Louise. He particularly loathed the Professor. He fantasized about a hurricane washing them all away and putting an end to their stupid antics. On the other hand, he couldn't quite bring himself either to turn it off or to call up something else. The show put a kind of Zen edge on his boredom. He was quite prepared, however, to make minor changes.

"Solarize out, please."

"This is a black and white video. I will have to impose simulated color."

There was something strange about the computer's voice. He would have to call the service, and that would put him further in hock. The machine was an AZU 2000 and well past its prime.

"Please do that."

The big wall screen became a glare of vibrating, strobing color. Gilligan, the Skipper, and a waddling duck were wading through a sea of violent, psychedelic orange and magenta.

"Off audio, please."

The sound of "Gilligan's Island" faded to nothing. Marlowe thought about the flat half liter of John Powers Irish in the bottom drawer of his desk. It was too early to start drinking. He also thought about the three Syrettes of Blind Tiger in the same drawer. It was certainly too early for that. Even half a deck of Blind Tiger and he'd be on his way down to the street, building up to act crazy. He coughed again.

"Goddamn it."

He stubbed out the cigarette. They packed so many chemicals into the damn things that they burned down like fast fuses. He took his time grinding the butt into the glass ashtray. The chipped red lettering around the outside read "George Washington Hotel." It was over a hundred years old, a genuine antique. Time was the constant malaise of the leisured out. You took your persona, your fantasy, your obsession, and your costume. You took the Guaranteed Income Maintenance and agreed to sterilization. You selected your new name and you moved into the Zone, Surf City, or one of the dozen or so other centers, and that was that. Permanent vacation. From then on, minute by minute, hour by hour—for the rest of your life—you had to wrestle with the problem of how you filled that time. Not that he would ever want to be a normal. The periods of boredom, the times when futility impacted, and the bouts of manic self-destruction were infinitely preferable to running like a standardized hamster on some corporate treadmill. Conformity was the cross that the normals had to bear: same clothes, same hair, same mannerisms, and same mindset. Normals smiled and strove. They toed the line and played on the team, and if they had any truck with fantasy, it was a guilty secret between them and either their assigned analysts or their therapy cells, depending on their corporate status. In the Zone all was fantasy.

The gold lettering on the opaque, plastiformed outer door said it all. MARLOWE—PRIVATE INVESTIGATOR & LICENSED POET. Of course, it was all Zone-style nonsense. He had never investigated anything, and there was no such thing as a licensed poet. It was a piece of original, self-conscious whimsy. In the early days there had, indeed, been a little poetry, but it had quickly faded away. In the Zone, creative endeavor always proved to be an act of vanity, an ultimate deadend. The only arts that flourished were those of performance and life-style. What really defined Marlowe was the trenchcoat, the dark, double-breasted, pinstripe suit, the two-tone shoes, and the battered fedora. He'd get in the electric reproduction Buick and drive to fortyist joints like the Brown Derby, the Radium, and the Club Noir, where he'd try to pick up women with padded shoulders and tiny hats with veils. For the rest of the time, he'd get drunk on straight John Powers; he'd deck Blind Tiger or squirt amdex; he'd squeal his car around the streets—as far as anyone could squeal a car that had a top speed of 40 kph—and scare hell out of the tourists. Now and again, he'd get involved in fistfights with others of his own kind or shootouts with nonlethal gas guns, but such behavior was exactly what was expected from anyone running a Humphrey Bogart life-style. It may have been a vapid and fundamentally worthless way of life, but some of the alternatives were quite unthinkable. He was profoundly grateful to whoever or whatever controlled his destiny that he had passed the twelve-plus test and had been allowed to leisure out. From his first days in school he had known that he was unemployable. His discipline quotient was all but nonexistent. If he'd failed the test, he would have wound up in one of the underclass ghettoes living on soyjacks and gin, or worse still, in one of the new control enclosures, wearing black and white pajamas and a prefrontal suppressor in the middle of his forehead.

The AZU 2000 was making a high-pitched chattering noise like an electronic chipmunk. Marlowe had never heard that sound before. He really did need to call the service.

"What's the matter with you?" he asked.

"I'm badly maintained and frivolously operated, and besides, this particular facility is rarely used."

When the service came, he'd have to have something done about the user petulance. It wasn't funny anymore.

"What facility?"

"Building security. You have an uninvited visitor."

"I never have uninvited visitors."

"She's at twenty-one and rising."

"She?"

"She."

"Is she good-looking?"

"How would I know?"

"Image her on the small screen."

There was something wrong with the camera in the elevator. It made the woman look as if she were underwater. Despite the effect, though, it was quite clear that she was extremely handsome. She was dressed forty—a scarlet suit with pencil skirt and a short tight jacket with padded shoulders. A matching pillbox hat was tilted forward on her head. Its veil stopped just below her eyes. As he shut off the large screen, blacking out the psychedelic images from "Gilligan's Island," Marlowe wondered about the woman's lingerie. Without thinking about it, he lit another cigarette.

"Close on her feet, please."

The shoes matched the suit. They had ankle straps and very high heels. She might have designed herself to his specifications.

"Now the face."

If one were talking perfection, her nose was a little too long, her eyes were too large, and her lips were too full. If one were talking attraction, she was perfection. Her makeup was exquisite.

Marlowe's voice had dropped to an awed whisper. "What the hell is this all about?"

The elevator came to a stop, and the woman stepped out of camera range. Marlowe wanted to take a belt from the bottle in the drawer, but there wasn't time.

"The visitor is at the door."

She actually knocked. That was cute. Slowly and deliberately, he leaned back in his chair. He swung his feet up onto the desk and crossed his legs at the ankles.

"Open, please."

The woman was in the small anteroom. "Marlowe?"

"In here."

In person, she was even more stunning than she'd been on the small screen. Marlowe was sorely tempted to compromise his image by jumping to his feet like a damned fool. In the Zone, a compromised image was worse than a deathwish. A deathwish could be quite acceptable in the right circumstances, while a compromised image could make a man a pariah. Musky perfume filled the room. Marlowe couldn't identify the brand. Ever since his nose had been broken, he wasn't good with perfumes. It didn't stop him from reacting to them, though. Something was stirring inside him that made it hard to maintain his pose of bored, cynical disinterest. He wondered if there were more in the room than just perfume. Was she raiding him with pheromones? It hardly seemed likely. A woman who looked the way she did had no need of endocrinal dirty tricks. She was standing on the other side of his desk. She looked slowly around the room at the shelves of personality-reinforcing junk that he had accumulated over the years, all the Chandler-era bric-a-brac that shored up his fantasy, like the worn and lumpy leather furniture, the scarred desk with its missing drawer handles and cigarette burns, and the mess of patchwork hardware. Marlowe was aware of how dusty everything was. The hosenose hardly worked anymore. Lately it had started crawling like a wounded spider. Another job for the service.

"You're Marlowe?" She'd finished her inspection and was looking at him. She had the expression of the unimpressed.

Marlowe nodded to the beat-up chair that was reserved for visitors. "Seat?"

As she sat, she crossed her legs in a way that Marlowe thought was hardly fair. If this was the start of a fantasy interface, she was coming on like gangbusters.

"What can I do for you, lady?"

"How much do you charge?"

It wasn't a question that women who played this kind of game usually asked. He picked the first number that jumped into his head. "Ten thousand a day in black scrip."

"That's ridiculous."

Marlowe smiled lazily. "You have to pay for the best."

"I'll pay you two thousand a day, regular."

"I don't dicker on the rate."

The game might be unorthodox, but it was coming along fine. Then she stopped it in its tracks.

"You can cut the crap, Marlowe. This isn't some fantasy interaction. This is the real thing."

Marlowe had been in the act of lighting a cigarette. He had struck a bookmatch one-handed, a trick that had taken weeks to perfect. The flame halted halfway to the tip of the cigarette. It burned down and scorched his thumb. He clumsily dropped it. In the Zone, nothing was the real thing, except maybe pain. It was also a waste of a match. The damn things were hard to find.

"What are you talking about?"

"I'm taking you at face value, Marlowe. My name is Veronica Stavers, and my sister Christine is missing. I want you to find her for me and I'm prepared to pay you two thousand a day for as long as it takes. Believe me, it's more than you're worth. Are you willing to take the job?''

Marlowe had recovered a little of his composure. The best thing would be to go along with the gag. ''You'll have to pay me in black. I'm a leisure-out. I can't handle regular.''

Black scrip was the Zone's guerilla currency. Leisure-outs weren't permitted to hold credit in excess of what was paid into their GIM accounts on the Ziapsu plan, the donated minimum wage of their proxy robots. It was never enough to maintain the fantasy, so there had to be an underground, off-data economy to make up the difference. It was particularly useful for illegal transactions where a record couldn't show. There was nothing tangible to back up black scrip. It only worked because of the mutual need and mutual interest of those who used it.

Veronica Stavers didn't seem fazed. ''I can work that out.''

''So what can you tell me about this sister of yours?''

Veronica Stavers opened a red patent shoulder bag that matched the rest of her ensemble. She produced a flat black disc and placed it on the desk. A holo, some fifteen centimeters tall. blossomed from the disc, showing a young woman in her early twenties, apparently at a party or maybe in a nightclub. She was wearing a short and very revealing cocktail dress; glass in hand, she was talking animatedly to someone outside the range of the holo. There was no doubt that she was Veronica Stavers's younger sister. The features came from the same mold, but where Veronica was controlled and businesslike, Christine sparkled and bubbled. Her figure was fuller and her hair was freaked out into an electric halo. Where Veronica might prove to be a challenge, Christine looked like more unashamed fun. There was, however, a pouty quality to her lower lip that might indicate a tendency to willful temper.

''Are there any more at home like you two?''

Veronica shook her head. ''A brother but no more sisters. One sister is quite enough.''

''How long ago was this taken?''

''Quite recently.''

''So she'll still look like this?''

"It's hard to know with Christine. She tends to be capricious about her image."

"That isn't too much help."

"She shouldn't have changed all that radically."

Marlowe reached for the holo. "Can I keep this?"

"That's what I brought it for."

As his hand touched the disc, the image faded. Marlowe dropped the disc in his pocket. "Where was she last seen?"

Once again, Veronica Stavers reached into her bag. This time she produced a small gold data cone. She held it out to Marlowe. "Can your equipment handle this?"

Marlowe took the cone. "Sure. I've got a universal reader. It's old, but it'll take this."

He turned the cone over in his fingers before he dropped it into the reader. "High-class packaging."

A street map that showed something like a four-mile-square section of the Zone appeared on the big screen. There were red symbols on a dozen or so locations, marking stores, tourist markets, and the more accessible night spots. Each was the kind of place that a normal, slumming in the Zone, might be expected to visit and drop some change. Beside each symbol there was a dialogue box with the details of an Amex transaction.

Marlowe raised an eyebrow. "You got hold of a detailed analysis of her Amex record? That stuff's supposed to be privacy guarded."

"I'm her sister, aren't I?"

"They don't normally give that information out, even to sisters. The only people who can get it are the cops and the government."

Veronica Stavers took a deep breath. For the first time she looked uncomfortable. "The family was sufficiently concerned that we hired a skater to go in and get it. I understand that Amex records aren't that hard to penetrate if you know what you're doing."

The Amex transactions spanned a period of about nine days, and the final one had been made exactly two weeks earlier. All but the one before the last were small to medium sums, just what a tourist would spend on souvenir purchases, bar bills, and the like. It was only the one before the last that fitted no recognizable pattern. It was a hundred and fifty thousand regular paid for what was minimally described as "raw data medium." This time Marlowe raised both eyebrows.

"Your sister spent one and a half biggies on blank ice?"

"The family didn't believe it either."

"You know the most obvious explanation for this?"

"You tell me."

"She changed the bundle from regular to black scrip."

"Why should she do that?"

"She was either paying for a couple of murders, a bunch of drugs, or she planned to go to ground in the Zone and wanted a little mad money."

"The family tends toward the last one. That's why we hired you."

Marlowe treated Veronica to a long, hard look. "Why did you hire me?"

"You're a native, you know the Zone."

Marlowe shook his head. "I can't buy that. You know what I am and that I only play at this. You'd be better off with a regular skip tracer."

"You're from here. You have natural cover. The family wants to keep this quiet."

"Natural cover? Is that why you came in here done up like a roaring forty? Are you sure this isn't some mightily overworked fantasy? What are you? A variation on Lauren Bacall in *The Big Sleep*?"

"Are you scared to do it for real once in your life?"

"Not me, lady. I just want to know what I'm dealing with." He gestured toward the screen. "See that last transaction? It was for the bill at a joint called Graceland. It's the one place on the list where tourists don't go. It's a greez joint, but it's on the edge of vampire turf. It strikes me that if she got to there, she was pretty entranced with the Zonelife. The most likely reason you haven't heard from her is that she's shacked up with some Zonee, and sooner or later she'll show up with a few bruises and mental scars and the whole clan can gather and kill the fatted calf. It happens all the time, but most families don't rush out and hire a leisured-out Bogart."

It was at that point that Marlowe's sixteen-pound Persian cat, Greenstreet, chose to make his entrance. He was fat, black, and amber-eyed, and was about the only living thing to which Marlowe was really attached. In an environment that was primarily fantasy, it was hard to form lasting relationships. There were times when Marlowe thought that the cat kept him sane. Greenstreet had been sleeping on top of the air conditioner. He woke, stretched, yawned, and jumped to the floor. He landed with a thud, then strolled over to Veronica Stavers and rubbed up against her stockings. He inadvertently gave her a few moments' breathing space.

"Nice cat."

"He's an amoral hustler, and you still haven't answered my questions."

"I told you. We hired you because you're from the Zone; you're on the inside, so to speak. If we hired a normal investigator, there'd be too much chance of the whole thing getting out. You don't know anyone in the normal world. With you, we're safe."

"You must be very fond of your sister to go to all this trouble."

"Mild dislike is about as good as it gets."

"So why bother to find her at all?"

Veronica seemed to be choosing her words carefully. "It's a matter of business."

"Business?"

"My grandfather built a very successful corporation. When he died two years ago, he left the bulk of the business to my brother Lawrence, but because he didn't altogether trust Lawrence, he also left blocks of voting stock and certain patents to both me and my sister. Right now the corporation is engaged in fighting off a hostile merger. Without her votes, we won't be able to do it. That's why she has to be found, and found quickly."

"Didn't your father or mother figure anywhere in the will?"

"My father and grandfather hated each other. He cut him out completely."

"Charming family."

Veronica Stavers's expression hardened. "I don't think you're in any position to pass judgment."

Marlowe shrugged. "I'll keep my mouth shut in the future."

"It might help."

"Is there anything else that I ought to know? Anything else in your box of goodies?"

Again Veronica hesitated. "There is one thing."

"Oh yeah?"

She took another cone out of her bag. This was a cheap black one. Marlowe held it up questioningly.

"So what's this?"

"It came through General Data. You'd better run it."

Marlowe dropped the cone into the reader. There was a waver of static, and then an image appeared on the big screen. Marlowe let out a low whistle. It was a homemade porno—crude, harsh light and a single camera, probably a robot, judging from the way it moved and angled. Christine Stavers had the starring role. Her hands and feet were tied with black rope, but she didn't look too upset about it. In fact, she seemed to be having the time of her life. Her costars were two men and another woman, but it was Christine who was getting all the attention. From their haircuts, tattoos, and cosmetic surgery, it was clear that they were vampires and they were being as creatively weird as only vampires could be.

"Does she do a lot of this sort of thing?"

"If you mean is she a slut, the answer's yes."

"And there was no note with this, no ransom demand, nothing like that?"

"Nothing."

"Maybe this is just her way of saying having a wonderful time, wish you were here."

"It struck us as a little elaborate. Almost as though she was trying too hard to convince us that she was hiding in the Zone."

"Meaning that she isn't in the Zone at all?"

"You never can tell with Christine. Maybe someone else is trying to throw us off the scent."

Marlowe glanced at the screen. "She hardly looks as though she's being coerced."

"Christine can find a way to enjoy most things."

"Do you have any idea when this might have been made?"

"From her hair, it must have been some time in the last couple of months."

Marlowe was thoughtful. "We can read all manner of stuff into this video and all it's going to do is confuse us. We have to take it on face value for the moment. On that level, all it tells us is that your sister goes to orgies with vampires."

"So what do you intend to do?"

Marlowe lit yet another cigarette. It gave him a moment to reflect. "Seems to me that we have to go back to the last place we know for sure that she was."

"Graceland?"

"Graceland."

"Should I come with you?"

"You want to go slumming, too?"

Veronica's lips compressed and her eyes were poisonous. "I don't think I like you, Marlowe."

"You don't have to. All you have to do is pay me, and I'll do my best to find your sister. How do I contact you?"

Veronica was back to the bag again. "Here's a number. I'd like to have regular reports."

What she gave him was old-fashioned, handmade notepaper. Maybe the Stavers family had even more money than he had first expected. There was a number but no address.

"Just so long as I don't show up in person."

"It would be better that way."

It was Marlowe's turn to look poisonous. "Don't worry, we leisure-outs know our place."

"Don't get me wrong, I'm not prejudiced."

Poison turned to merely bleak. "Tell me about it."

It was always the same with the natural rich. Personally I don't have anything against you people, but what would the neighbors think? No wonder she'd turned up in forty drag. It wasn't camouflage, it was insulation. She wasn't emotionally equipped to walk through the Zone as herself. Now she was preparing to leave. "I'll wait to hear from you."

"What about my money?"

Veronica was on her feet. She paused. "Oh, yes. I'll get it to you by messenger—a three-day retainer. It should be here in two hours."

"Then I'll start work in three."

After she was gone, Marlowe looked around for Greenstreet. ''So what do you think of that?''

But Greenstreet had gone back to the top of the air conditioner.

TWO

THE GREEZ LIKED IT LOUD AND FLASHING. THEY LIKED neon and lasers and stainless steel and chrome. They liked sculptured hair and huge, gyrating holos of their twentieth-century icons. They also liked to dance. As Marlowe walked down the wide sweep of stairs that led from the nightclub entrance to the heart of the bright darkness, the dance floor was dominated by a twenty-meter-tall image of Ann-Margret doing what looked like the Watusi to a dyged-up Buddy Holly song played close to the pain threshold. Almost like a pagan idol, she was surrounded by her worshipers, a hundred or more figures copying her every move. The image was primarily green and magenta, and the colors were reflected in the oiled hair of the men and the metal accessories of both sexes. With each step, highbrights flashed at Marlowe from the underside of the treads. The first three dazzled him, but after that he established a rhythm: step, blink, step, blink. Marlowe didn't particularly want to be noticed, but his pride wouldn't allow him to actually dress up greez. Once a forty, always a forty. His only compromise was that he'd left the trenchcoat, the mask, and the fedora in the coatcheck. With a black shirt and a white tie, he figured that he'd at least marginally mingle with some of the early enders, the ones who included Hank Williams in their pantheon.

Unfortunately, he seemed to have figured wrong. Halfway down the stairs, a group of five greez were leaning on the lucite balustrade, stomping their feet on the treads so the highbrights flashed in time with the music. There were four men and a woman. The men were almost identical in black leather, white spandex, and silver chains. Their triangular sideburns reached their jawlines, and their conical pompadours extended maybe twenty centimeters in front of their foreheads. The woman wore a hooped skirt, and her obviously amplified breasts were crammed into a plastic bustier. Her beehive was so lavish that it made her a good head taller than the men.

The woman spotted him first. She spat on the floor and sneered. "Stinking forty, why don't you piss off back to the Brown Derby!"

Marlowe could only assume that his hair had given him away. Not that it mattered all that much. Graceland, being so close to vampire country, was fairly tolerant of outsiders. There were much more territorial greez joints, like Good Golly Miss Molly or Screamin' Jay's, where they wouldn't even bother to insult and would just get straight to work with gravity knives and razor chains. Graceland even let in vampires. A small knot of them, white-faced zombies in their black capes and high-spiked hair, stood at the edge of the dance floor, sinister and motionless amid the ducking and weaving greez. Vampires didn't dance. They froze and stared, and their pleasures ran to endodrene, dark multiple sex, and occasional outbursts of frenzied, mindless violence. Their favorite weapons were wrist flowers, shirakin, finger blades, and butterfly knives. There were some who'd had long steel fangs implanted in their upper jaws. As Marlowe passed them, two pairs of eyes flashed, one red, the other amber. These were another piece of surgery favored by the vampires: clusters of microleds, implanted in the back of the eye socket so, when activated, they'd shine out through the pupil.

The relationship between greez and vampires was a strange one. On the surface, they were opposite extremes, neon and ice, and yet their was a certain kinship between the two leisure-out subcultures. They both went to the limit with their personal theater, and they even shared common roots. Their cultures met on some dark, timeless bayou where Baron Samedi and Jerry Lee Lewis lived as one.

The walls had started pulsing shocking pink. "Heartbeat, why do you skip when my baby kisses me?" Buddy Holly was still distorting down a century. Marlowe knew that the way the glowing pink walls were expanding and contracting was pure illusion, but it still made him a little nauseated. He felt like an organ parasite and was glad that he hadn't had anything to drink. Jayne Mansfield had replaced Ann-Margret. She was walking her preposterous walk but getting nowhere. She had two quarts of milk in old-fashioned glass bottles clutched beneath her breasts. Marlowe negotiated another gang of greez. This bunch merited avoidance. They were androgynous figures in black, thigh-length, platform boots and short coats with built-up, tuck-and-roll shoulders. Their faces were covered with chrome masks, identical portraits of Elvis Presley in his prime. To Marlowe, they were the most alien of fantasies, hunched black insects with the faces of hood ornaments. They were beyond the border, beyond sex, probably beyond drugs and certainly beyond help. Marlowe was glad that he had one reliable contact in the place. He would have hated to start his first real investigation talking to those cold chrome masks.

Leroy Strange was a one-time zooter with conked hair and a pencil mustache who had traded suits, turned himself into Little Richard, and become Graceland's number-one personality bartender. Back in his zoot days he'd hung out at the Club Noir, and he and Marlowe had established a certain rapport based on a common taste for Blind Tiger. If anyone in Graceland would give Marlowe a fair shake, it was Leroy Strange.

The bartender looked amazed and possibly a little less than pleased as Marlowe eased his way through the crowd of greez around the bar. "What the hell are you doing here, Marlowe? You're a long way from your usual haunts. A stone forty like you don't belong in a place like this. You'll end up getting into a mess of trouble, and I ain't going to help you out."

"Just give me a drink, Leroy."

"Don't have no John Powers. Just Suntory down the pipe."

"That'll do."

Leroy Strange passed Marlowe a straight shot of scotch in a frozeglass. "It's on the house, Marlowe, on account of all that Tiger we decked in the old days. All I want to know is what you're doing in this place."

"I'm working on a case."

Leroy Strange looked at him with something little short of contempt. "Shit, Marlowe. What kind of fucked-up fantasy is this? Have you lost your mind?"

"It's no fantasy, Leroy. This is for real. Some rich normal lost her sister in the Zone and she wants me to find her."

"So you lost your amateur status?"

"It looks like it."

"Oh, my soul."

"Can I show you something?"

"As long as you don't whip out your dick."

Marlowe took the holo disc that Veronica Stavers had given him from his pocket and placed it on the bar. The image of Christine Stavers came to life. Leroy immediately tried to cover it with his hands.

"Turn that goddamn thing off before it gets someone annoyed."

Already a tall greez in black highrise pants and a red drape jacket was scowling in his direction. Marlowe shut the holo down.

"You know her?"

"Is that the bitch you're looking for?"

"Uh-huh."

"I wish you luck. She came in here and caused more trouble than a squad of marines on amdex."

"So what happened?"

"It must have been about two weeks ago, she comes in here quite early in the evening, dressed norm but already loaded on about everything you could think of. I mean, she was messed up—and bent on getting worse. The weirdest thing of all was that there were a bunch of vams with her. Not the ones who come in here. Cold suckers, the kind who usually never leave the territory.

And they're around her like they were bodyguards or something."

Leroy Strange paused to serve another customer.

"Now, since I ain't never heard of no norm hiring no inner-circle vams to tour-guide her 'round the Zone, I figured they must be letting her run on account of how they have some very bizarre plans for her. Which means, Marlowe, that if you find her, she ain't going to be quite the same as when she left home."

He poured some more drinks.

"Anyway, she's drinking it up and getting worse and worse, falling out of her dress and doing the whole drunk-norm bit clear to the edge. By two o'clock, she's so rowdy that even the rockos are getting pissed off, and you know how they like to romp and stomp. Thing is, though, the vams are still with her, and since they ain't walked away from her, I can only think that whatever black vam plans they got for her are real serious. Not that I care too much. What I'm really thinking about is that I better throw her ass out of the joint before someone starts carving their name on her. Nobody cares if we cut up each other, but a dead or bleeding norm can start the chillgrief coming down."

"And did you throw her out?"

"That was the lacklogic weird. Just as I was looking around for the bouncers to give her the heave, the vams whisk her away."

"And that was the last you saw of her?"

"That was it, and I didn't want to see her again. I guess if you want to find her you're going to have to start looking in vam town. Once again, I wish you luck."

Marlowe nodded. If Christine Stavers had vanished into vampire territory he was going to need luck. On the dance floor there was an outbreak of cheering. A holo of the young Elvis Presley had risen to its full height.

Marlowe had left the reproduction Buick back in the underground parking lot of the apartment building. This close to vampire country, there was too much chance of it being vandalized, and he loved the electric car almost as much as he loved Greenstreet. The sight of its chrome ripped off or its paintwork covered in graffiti would kill him. He retrieved his coat, hat, and mask from the coatcheck. For a few moments, Marlowe stood in the shelter of the club's awning, smoked a cigarette, and watched the fiber optic sign change color. Three vampires on the sidewalk watched him with blank, corpse-white faces but made no move. Finally he flicked the butt into the gutter, fastened his mask, and started walking. His mask was made of form-fitting black latex. Someone had once told him that it made him look like the Spirit.

The air was thick with something that was more than fog but not quite rain. The temperature hadn't dropped any, and he was sweating inside his Burberry despite the built-in coolants. It was a bad night. Sheets of static that might later become a full-blown electric storm played around the downtown towers. Marlowe couldn't see any hacks, but for the moment he didn't care. He had a lot of thinking to do and he thought better when he was walking. It was really only just starting to sink in that all this was real, that it was no fantasy, no piece of self-theater. His first impulse was to return Veronica Stavers's money and tell her to forget the whole thing. He wasn't going to spend the next few days risking his ass in vampire town looking for some screwed-up normal. His second impulse was not to return Veronica Stavers's money, and to move deeper into the Zone where she wouldn't be able to find him. Beyond the impulses, however, there was an awakening pride. After a life on the scrap heap, playing like a child, he actually had something to do. It might be a no-good gig, but it was a gig and it was his. He was no longer pretending, and after a lifetime of make believe, reality was extremely seductive. The money was also a consideration. He had the three-day retainer, but it was quite likely that the search for Christine Stavers would run longer. Two thousand a day would do a lot to fix his decaying electronics and his malfunctioning robots. The one snag was the matter of the vampires. If Christine had indeed taken up with a vam gang, he had problems. The vampires were strange and unpredictable. They had their roots in the punk rockers of the late twentieth century, but they had gathered a lot more gothic fantasies along the way until they had become near alien in their studied weirdness. They were an almost completely closed society, and their hostility toward outsiders was legendary. The only approach open to Marlowe was the direct one. He would, quite literally, have to walk into vam town, knock on the front door, and start asking if anyone had seen Christine. He didn't relish the prospect.

For the first few blocks, Marlowe had been walking down empty streets with only derelicts and garbage for company and the undertow of traffic noise and half-heard music as background for his thoughts, but now the lights of Avenue J, the main strip on the east side of the Zone, were reflected on the wet sidewalk. Despite the foul weather, the strip was crowded. In the Zones people would tolerate almost anything to avoid the sense of being penned up in their apartments. On the street there was always the chance of something happening. Inside four walls, a person was alone with his needs.

Marlowe put his speculations on the back burner as he started to make his way down the strip. Survival in the Zone depended on keeping one's instincts to the fore. Preoccupation could be dangerous. The levels of frustration, anger, and neurosis in the area were sufficiently high that one always had to be on guard, particularly as those emotions were frequently coupled with drugs or implant stimulation. Just to prove the point, a gang of naziboys in mirror masks, duckbill caps, and swastikas were hanging around outside a foolfeel parlor, harassing the patrons coming in and out. They seemed to feel that the varied cortsim sex substitutes offered inside were somehow against what they considered to be the natural order of things. There was a certain irony in the fact that on another night they might just as easily be found making trouble for the street hookers, the girls and boys who sold traditional body sex. On the other hand, though, nobody really expected consistency from naziboys. They were a universal pain in the ass, stunted bundles of hate masquerading as a political philosophy. Even their mirror masks were a kind of mute hostility. Looking into their faces, all one saw was one's own features superimposed on a black naziboy uniform. Marlowe quickly crossed the street as a handful of heavies emerged from the foolfeel parlor and went to work on the nazis with boots and billy clubs. The sight of dark fighting figures in front of the foolfeel facia, an undulating screen of moving erotic abstracts, was archetypical of the Zone. The glowing, featureless flesh shapes moved against each other while black silhouettes kicked out and flailed. There was a ripple of applause from passersby as the naziboys took to their heels.

The prostitutes were out in force. The necessity of masks in the greenhouse weather made for some exotic figures and also a certain degree of pig-in-poke risk for the clientele. Animals and birds seemed to be a particular, momentary vogue. One young woman was naked but for a huge, blue and yellow butterfly mask, a scant black bikini, high spike heels, and a short transparent rain cape. Her body glistened with moisture. She inquired if Marlowe wanted to go out. After a moment's hesitation, he shook his head. He wasn't in the mood for automatic hooker sex. There was also a paradox with whores in the Zone. It was impossible to tell which were regular hustlers and which were leisure-outs acting their way through a time-honored fantasy. A lot of the time, it didn't matter too much, but there were occasions when the ones who were in it for the fun could go to some very alarming extremes.

As well as the prostitutes, there was also a heavy sprinkling of solo weirds. Where the majority of the fantasy leisure-outs formed themselves into definable groups like greez, forties, bounders, and the rest, there were others who went their lone sweet way. A Harpo Marx tooted his horn at a disdainful trio of kamikaze blondes. A figure in a full space suit stared at the animated displays outside a domination joint, while a very drunk San Diego chicken had some difficulty crossing the road. A police gunship clattered overhead, flanked by two drone ultralights. Normally the cops didn't bother too much about what went on in the Zone, short of riot or mass murder. They were only present because it was game night in the old stadium and the back entrance to the stadium opened onto the far end of the strip. The games must have been near to their conclusion. It was possible to hear the roar of the crowd above all the competing noises on the strip. Very soon, fifty thousand normals would be surging out of the stadium, limp from three hours of gratuitous violence, desperate to get back to their high-rise suburbs. The cops were there to make sure they weren't raped, robbed, or picked on before they reached the safety of the tunnels.

There was some kind of party going on at the gin joint on the corner of 208th. It looked as though it had been roaring for some hours, and a number of the revelers had spilled out onto the street, swaying like the blood brain barriers were breaking down. The tavern, which rejoiced in the uncomplicated name of John's, wasn't strictly themed to any particular group, but there were a number of forties among its regulars and there were certainly a few in with the stumblers on the sidewalk. Marlowe thought that he recognized two women. They were a pair of sisters, called Nora and Charlene, dye-job redheads from the Minnie Mouse end of things. He had slept with both of them more than once, and one time with both of them together. They were loud, uncomplicated fun, but he generally wanted them to leave in the morning. They called out to him as they approached.

"Hey, Marlowe! Is that you?"

Marlowe peeled off his mask. "Sure is. How are you two doing?"

He was being embraced by two sets of arms.

"We're drunk, Marlowe. We've been drinking and decking all night. You going to join the party?"

Marlowe shook his head. "I've got stuff to do in the morning that wouldn't be helped by a hangover."

Nora had her face very close to his. "What's the matter with you, Marlowe? You on a case?"

Charlene giggled. "You don't have to do that stuff with us, Marlowe. You know we love you."

"Yeah, Marlowe. Come and get loaded. We've missed you."

Marlowe's newfound professional pride wavered. There was conscientious and there was just plain dumb. He linked arms with Nora and Charlene and went into John's.

When he eventually reached home, Greenstreet regarded him balefully. The cat had been fed by the robot tender, and he hated the tender. He considered any attempt by the tender to look after him as a personal insult and definite neglect on Marlowe's part. Marlowe felt awful enough; he didn't need the animal's reproaches. It was mid-morning and he had two basic options in front of him. He could crawl into bed and sleep away the rest of the day, or he could take a shower, swallow a handful of pills and a couple of squirts, and head straight out for vampire country. Sleeping was certainly not what Veronica Stavers was paying him for, and although the second option was totally lacking in charm, it had the consolation that with his nervous system turned into a battleground between the stims and his hangover, he'd probably be so coldwired that he wouldn't remember to be frightened. The vampires might well respect that. Reluctantly, he stripped off his clothes and stepped into the shower.

He discovered to his disgust that the water was out and he had to make do with half a pack of chemical wipes. Fortunately, he had an ample supply of drugs. After a half deck of Blind Tiger, four blue octagons, and three squirts from an amdex haler, his eyeballs were threatening to revolve but he was on his feet and motoring. His first move was to call Veronica Stavers at the number she'd given him and report what he'd learned from Leroy Strange. It was hardly conclusive, but she might as well know that he was earning his money. He particularly stressed the risk that he was running by taking the investigation into vampire country, but she didn't seem terribly impressed. His next move was to open the secret compartment under his mattress and take out his one lethal weapon. As lethal weapons went this one was a dandy, a laser-sighted Smith & Wesson Reaper, an over-and-under machine pistol. The top barrel fired 10mm self-propelled; the bottom was a seven-gauge shotgun. If anything was going to keep the vampires at bay, it was this little beauty. He dropped the Reaper into the specially constructed shoulder holster and closed the seal on his trenchcoat. He patted the still sulking Greenstreet.

"Don't wait up."

Marlowe's best idea was to go into vampire country in the middle of the day. Part of the mystique was that they were almost completely nocturnal, and as he crossed the line that divided their acknowledged turf from the rest of the Zone, the streets were virtually deserted. The hard core of vampire town was a dozen blocks of crumbling, nineteenth-century tenements. Even at high noon, it was a dark, sinister neighborhood. Every surface was covered in black unintelligible graffiti, not only on street level but all the way up to the rooftops. There were even huge cabalistic symbols painted across the streets and sidewalks. The black spraypaint reached to the most inaccessible walls and overhangs. The vampires weren't only obsessive, they were also agile. The overall patina of graffiti somehow gave the buildings the look of being diseased. Sagging ropes of cable, like the webs of some monster spider, were strung from roof to roof, and the roofs themselves were festooned with satellite dishes and all manner of aerials. The vampires were nothing if not high tech.

Not every vampire was asleep in his or her coffin. Somewhere there was music playing, a modal dirge from the doomboom of the twenty twenties. There were also movements in among the roof aerials that suggested that his progress was being monitored by a series of lookouts. Marlowe felt like the lone scout advancing into Indian territory.

One of the main focal points of the neighborhood was a place called The Bat Cave. Marlowe had decided that it would be the most obvious door on which to knock. It had originally been a traditional Irish bar and after that it had been a zippie hangout, but now it was something entirely vampire. The whole front of the building was one enormous and incredibly complex mural. It was a strange marriage of El Greco and monster movies. Leather-winged nightcrawlers grappled with fanged corpse women. Chained and naked maidens were sacrificed by cowled priests while red hellfire blazed from rocky fissures and lightning struck down at gothic cathedrals. Marlowe stood and stared at the mural for a full minute before he took a deep breath, unglued his mask, unsealed his trenchcoat so the Reaper was plainly visible, and pushed open The Bat Cave's huge, iron-bound door. He was glad that he felt no pain.

For the first few seconds he could hardly see a thing. After broad daylight, the gloom was close to absolute. The main room of The Bat Cave was long and narrow.

The original bar had long since been torn out, but the place still had a little of that ambiance. A set of flat color cathodes arranged on the end wall to resemble a stained-glass window added a certain ecclesiastical air. An antique lava lamp pulsed in an alcove, a half-dozen candles guttered in a cast-iron holder, and, rather incongruously, a large, neon, Kirin beer dragon flashed on and off. These were all the lights there were, and each cast its own set of sinister shadows.

Gradually, Marlowe's eyes adjusted. There were six vampires in the place, but none of them seemed inclined to make a move toward him. A couple, male and female, lay together in a beat-up, high-backed couch, entwined and engrossed. A male with bleached white hair that rose from his head straight up for almost a foot sat alone at a table. There was a small, black GD stim box in front of him with leads running to implanted spike receptors in his forearm. He was clearly in a world of his own. Two other males lounged at another table, drinking beer and regarding Marlowe with bored insolence. One of them had a shaved head and ears that had been surgically tailored to long, upswept points. In the corner of the room there was a steel cage designed for one occupant; a young vampire girl sat inside on a bench, smoking a cigar, seemingly unconcerned by her incarceration. There were more murals that looked as though they had been painted by the same artist or artists who had done the one on the outside of the building. There were more gothic movie monsters, sado porn of graphic severity, and portraits of some of their cultural icons—Jim Morrison, Morthland, Lord Byron, Bela Lugosi, Bradford Hess, Ed Gein, John Lydon, and Freddie the Psycho. The vampires had a choice assortment of heroes. Somewhere there was music playing at low volume. It sounded like Mahler. *Das Kindertotenlieder?* Mahler was hardly Marlowe's forte, but it fitted with the vampire fantasy as well as anything else: The children are dead.

Marlowe had no comprehensive plan of action. When he'd set out, the only thing he'd had in mind was to make it to The Bat Cave and see what happened when he got there. Now he was there and nothing was happening. He was hardly inclined to walk up to any of the denizens of the place and start asking private-eye questions. That was simply the wrong approach. It was time to be a psychologist, not a cop. Except who could predict vampire psychology? Marlowe walked tentatively toward an empty table against the wall. Still nobody made a move. Marlowe sat down. He let his coat fall open so that the Reaper was in easy reach and in even more plain sight. He took the holo disc from his pocket and placed it on the table in front of him. The image of Christine Stavers came alive. Marlowe was getting sick of looking at it. The girl in the cage giggled. The couple looked up briefly and then went back to what they were doing. The vampire wired into the stim box took no notice whatsoever. The only real reaction came from the two boys swilling beer. The one with the shaved head and pointed ears slowly stood up. He grinned at Marlowe. As well as altered ears, he had long, implanted canine teeth. The other one pulled out a pack of Kenyan Marlboroughs and lit one with the air of a man who was settling down to watch the show. The bald vampire walked slowly toward Marlowe, still grinning. Very slowly, Marlowe's hand crept toward the butt of the Reaper.

The vampire reached the table. Close up, the grin was dangerously insane; Marlowe, with his nervous system jangling, was sorely tempted to remove it with a blast of self-propelled 10mms. He resisted the temptation with great difficulty, telling himself firmly that it was no way to start an investigation. The vampire leaned forward and slowly passed a hand through the image of Christine Stavers. He made a soft hissing sound and repeated the gesture with the other hand. Marlowe didn't think it was possible, but the wolf grin widened. His gun hand started to twitch, but then the vampire pushed himself away from the table. Marlowe was surprised. He'd been certain that there was going to be some sort of violence. His relief was short-lived, however. The bald vampire walked across the room and picked up an old-fashioned wall phone. He was talking too softly for Marlowe to hear what he was saying. When he was through, he returned to his beer. He and his companion both sat staring at Marlowe as though expecting something to happen, both wearing the same feral, lupin grin. Marlowe had to assume that reinforcements had been summoned and that the two vampires were waiting with anticipatory glee. The glee worried him. Maybe he should cut his losses and get the hell out of the whole situation. What were the reinforcements going to be like? Only pride and drugs kept him in his seat. He was damned if he was going to be grinned down by those two weird assholes across the room.

The door swung open and the light streamed in like a shock. Marlowe tensed. Three figures were silhouetted in the doorway. The middle one was at least a head taller than the other two, but they all cast long shadows across the floor.

"I am Yorga. What do you want here?"

"I'm Marlowe and I've been hired to find a missing woman."

The door swung closed. Marlowe had avoided looking directly at the light, so now he could see the newcomers. If there was such a thing as a king of the vampires, Yorga had to be it. He was at least seven feet tall, most likely the product of preteen artificial growth. His parent or parents must have been in on the act. Conceivably, he was even a second generation. His skin was the color of parchment that had been stored under a rock. Aside from his size, Yorga was loaded down with gimmicks. He was one of the most highly customized human beings that Marlowe had ever seen. He was shrouded in a full black opera cape with a stand-up collar that framed his face and would have done credit to the wardrobe of Ming the Merciless. The cape was shot with light threads that coiled and roiled in vague but definitely serpentine patterns. His hair was slicked back at the sides and dyed pale blue. It darkened to the center and rose to a high crest that added another nine inches to his height. His eyes were lensed over and flashed the same blue. The silver tips of his heavy engineer boots were studded with shock caps that could probably knock over an ox if he kicked it. As he confronted Marlowe, he swept back the cape in a deliberately dramatic gesture, revealing a black vinyl bodysuit that left his arms bare. His arms were his most striking feature. It wasn't just the maze of tattoos that duplicated in miniature the graffiti on the buildings.

He had more hooked into those arms than the average patient on an operating table. There was a stim block strapped to each wrist with lines going to a switchboard of receptors and a row of timedose dermals running all the way up to his biceps. A third stim block hung from his neck by a silver chain; the lines went to receptors at his throat. With so much medication and direct neural stimulation running into his system, it was amazing that the man had even a nodding acquaintance with any kind of reality. And yet he seemed perfectly in control. Yorga was either a superman or a monster, if indeed there was any difference. The worst shock was when he smiled. He had a mouthful of gold fangs.

"Marlowe? You're called Marlowe?"

Marlowe slowly nodded. He was starting to think that he might already be history. He placed both hands flat on the table. "Right. Marlowe."

"Tell me, Marlowe, are you stupid, crazy, or suicidally brave?"

"I'm doing a job."

"You'd follow a forty fantasy all the way into my country?"

"This is no fantasy. I've been hired by this woman's family to find her. The last time she was seen, it was in the company of vampires. I look where I have to."

"Did they hire you to bring a Smith & Wesson Reaper into my country? Have you come to kill vampires, Marlowe? Is that your fantasy, Marlowe? Are you the fearless vampire killer? It's a strange fantasy for a forty."

Marlowe had the patience of a man on borrowed time. "I already told you that I'm looking for this woman. The Reaper is strictly for protection. I want to get out of here alive."

"And do you think you will?"

"I'm hoping."

"Do you think you can shoot your way out of here?"

Marlowe could feel himself sweating. If his hands hadn't been pressed flat on the table, they would have been shaking. "If I was threatened, I'd kill you first."

"You think I can be killed, Marlowe?"

"I figure if I blew your head off you'd be effectively dead. Immortality is your fantasy. All I see is an over-stim.'' If he was going to go, he might as well go with class.

Yorga suddenly laughed. If lizards laughed, they'd laugh like Yorga. ''You amuse me, Marlowe.''

He pointed to the holo of Christine Stavers. ''Turn that thing off.''

Marlowe cut off the holo.

Yorga stroked one of the lines running into his throat. ''That woman is starting to get on my nerves.''

So she was there. The girl in the cage giggled loudly. The woman who had come in with Yorga hissed at her and spun the razor flowers on her wrists into the fighting position.

''You shut your mouth, Carmila, or you'll be worse than caged.''

Carmila giggled again. ''I like being caged. You know I can enjoy anything. That's why you love me.''

Yorga's eyes flashed blue. ''Shut up, both of you.''

Marlowe had been so occupied with Yorga that he'd had no time to pay attention to his two companions. The one on the right was male but anonymous in a full-head, black leather mask. He was of more than average height but was dwarfed by Yorga. The woman was also tall. Right at that moment, she was demurely folding away the razor flowers. She had gone to a lot of trouble to make herself look like a living corpse. Her already large eyes were made huge by rings of black and purple, her lips were blue, and her dead black hair was scraped back from a high white forehead and hung straight to her waist. Like Yorga, she wore a skintight black bodysuit, only in her case, her arms were covered. She appeared to have no built-in stims unless they were concealed in the suit, and Marlowe didn't see how that was possible when it fitted her slim figure so closely. While Marlowe was looking at her, the woman was also examining him. There was something in her expression that he didn't like. She glanced at Yorga.

''If you don't want to kill him yourself, can I have him?''

The girl in the cage started again. ''Why can't I have him? She gets everything.''

Yorga glared at each of them in turn. "I may not want to kill him."

That was the best news that Marlowe had heard since he'd arrived in vampire country. Unfortunately, the woman with Yorga continued to protest.

"You can't let him go. He'll tell the rest of the Zone that it's possible to walk into our neighborhood, armed and uninvited, and get out alive."

"I said I may not want to kill him."

"It would be a sign of weakness."

"Don't argue with me, Morticia."

"It would still be a sign of weakness."

"It would be a sign that we are totally unpredictable, and that has always been our tradition." He turned his attention to Marlowe. "I'm going to let you go."

"I appreciate that."

"You'd better, because if I hear you're going around boasting that you got the better of Yorga, I'll come and find you."

Morticia wasn't finished. "You're a fool, Yorga. He's obviously going to tell everyone that the vampires let him go."

Yorga's hand shot out like a striking snake and grabbed Morticia by the throat. Marlowe was quite amazed at his speed.

"Don't ever speak to me like that!"

Morticia's eyes were twice their original size. Her fingers flexed as though she were restraining herself from opening her razor flowers and gutting Yorga. She probably would have gone white with fury, except with her cadaverlike complexion it was scarcely possible. For a long moment, the two of them glared at each other. Marlowe wondered about interpersonal relations between vampires. They had to be complex in a world of razors, cages, and surgical outrage. Finally Morticia's arms dropped to her sides. She relaxed, clearly letting go of her fury. Yorga released her, then rounded on Marlowe.

"You'd better get out of here before I change my mind."

Marlowe knew that he was taking his life in his hands, but his newfound pride refused to lie down. "What about the woman I came to find?"

The man in the black mask spoke for the first time. His voice was overlaid with a rasping, electronic distortion. It sounded as though his throat were stuffed with tinfoil. "She said that someone might come looking for her. I don't think she imagined that it would be a forty Bogart."

Yorga grinned gold at him and then turned back to Marlowe. "You've got a lot of gall for one whose life has just been spared."

Marlowe spread his hands in self-deprecation. Yorga's eyes, which had been burning bright blue since the exchange with Morticia, slowly dimmed.

"Christine Stavers is under my protection. She paid me to conceal her, and I'll go on concealing her until she leaves of her own accord or she makes me crazy. You can tell that to her family."

Marlowe didn't care to speculate on how much it took to make Yorga crazy or what form that craziness might take. "I didn't know vampires took bodyguard contracts."

"We all need money, Marlowe. Now get out of here."

Back in the daylight, Marlowe experienced a violent reaction. His whole body shook. Both drugs and courage were wearing off. The daylight itself wasn't up to much. In fact, it wasn't much brighter than the gloom inside The Bat Cave. A khaki overcast was moving in, threatening a massive downpour. Mid-afternoon was turning into an oppressive twilight. Marlowe took one final look at the mural on the front of The Bat Cave, then walked away at a brisk pace. He wanted nothing more than to get back to his apartment, make his peace with Greenstreet, and sleep through the impending comedown.

He had thought that the sense of being watched would go away once he had crossed the line out of vampire territory. To his dismay, it didn't. He told himself repeatedly that it was just the drugs' last kickings, but he couldn't shake an uneasy urge to keep looking over his shoulder. He heard a car behind him and glanced back in the hope that it might be one of the Zone's few-and-far-between cabs. It turned out to be the complete antithesis of a beat-up Zone hack. Black and shiny, it was a big limousine with mirror windows. It was too far away for Marlowe to identify, but he thought it looked like a late-model Mercedes. What the hell was a car like that doing in the Zone?

The engine gunned and the car accelerated toward him. From the sound of the engine, he realized that it wasn't an electric car. It had the roar of a full-blown hydro burner. The presence of the car was so incongruous that Marlowe turned and stared as it roared down the empty street. When it was only twenty or thirty meters from him, it swerved. It swung inward and its nearside front wheel mounted the sidewalk. The car was coming for him, deliberately trying to run him down. For a second, he froze in horror, then self-preservation took over. There was a recessed doorway beside him. Marlowe dived and rolled. He hit hard and awkwardly. He knew that he had done something bad to his shoulder, but there was no time for pain. The limo grazed the wall, ruining its paint job and throwing off sparks. Someone wanted extremely badly to kill him. He jerked his feet up and the car screeched by, missing him by a handsbreadth.

The car screamed forward for another twenty meters, then the unseen driver slammed on the brakes, the back end came up, and the engine protested as it was thrown into reverse. The black limo was coming back for another try. Marlowe fumbled out the Reaper. The Mercedes was angling to rear-end him in the doorway. It really was a Mercedes. The three-spoke wheel insignia was all too clear and coming down on him fast. Marlowe opened fire, pressing himself back into the doorway. He let go with both barrels—four blasts of the seven-gauge and a stream of 10mms. The rear window shattered, and the shock must have thrown the driver off his turn. Instead of bringing the car into the doorway, he slammed it hard against the wall, crumpling the trunk. The engine howled again and the wheels spun and smoked as it went back to drive. Marlowe braced himself for another attack, knowing it was hard to stop a determined car with a machine pistol. To his suprise, it kept on going. It raced down the street, laid rubber on a turn, and was gone. Marlowe stepped out of the doorway in total shock. Spectators were starting to emerge from nearby buildings. Nobody approached him. The still-smoking gun must have put them off.

Marlowe was at a complete loss. This was just too much reality in one day. Twice in one afternoon, he had expected to die. With the vampires, it was understandable—he had known he was running a risk confronting them on their own turf. A black Mercedes trying to crush him to hamburger was a whole different matter. A homicidal normal out killing Zonees at random? Correction. A rich homicidal normal—a car like that ought to rate a chauffeur. It made no sense unless the black Mercedes was somehow connected with the Staverses, a deluxe version of the old get-off-the-case-shamus routine. If that was so, and he had a gut feeling that it was, the business had turned on him and was threatening to swallow him in one gulp. He didn't even know why. Although it was tempting, he wasn't quite ready to get off the case. The idea of his being arbitrarily squished by an expensive auto made him mad. On the other hand, though, before he went any further he intended to find out a great deal more about the Stavers family. The one person in the Zone who might have that kind of information was Joshua Long.

THREE

"IT ALL HINGES ON TWO THINGS: ENERGY AND POPulation. We never made any serious attempts to check the population growth until it was far too late, and we burned energy like there was no tomorrow. Now there may not be a tomorrow. Two hundred years of burning hydrocarbons started the planet going greenhouse. Our brief romance with nuclear power gave us the disasters at Chernobyl, Dungeness, Indian Point, and then that whole string of cheap third-world reactors that the industrial nations foisted on them at the same time they were closing down their own programs. Huge tracts of land were rendered unusable for thousands of years along with the bits of Chile and Argentina that glow in the dark after their little atomic tussle. Diseases mutated faster than we could find cures for them. DX virus and acid rain wiped out most of the Amazon rain forest, and that just happened to be the main natural atmospheric recycling plant. In two hundred years, we'll have an atmosphere like Venus. Having fouled up our nest, our only hope seems to be to move to another tree."

Joshua Long tended to pontificate. Marlowe had let him run on for a while, but now it was time to bring him back to the point.

"This is all very depressing, but what does it have to do with the Stavers family?"

"Elias Stavers was one of the first individuals to realize that our only hope was to get off the planet. Before him, all space research was either military or to boldly go where no man had gone before."

Marlowe was stunned. "That Stavers?"

"It never occurred to you?"

"Why should it have? I thought when Veronica Stavers hired me she was talking about a small family business, not a giant aerospace corporation."

"A giant, independent, aerospace corporation. That's the key to the Staverses."

"Huh?"

"You're into something way over your head, Marlowe."

Joshua Long was a major oddity in the Zone. He was also a major power. Physically he was unimpressive—a small, lumpy potato of a man with wispy blond hair, he was a virtual gnome in a stained purple windbreaker and drab tan pants. The only thing that marked him as someone special were his penetrating blue eyes, which never seemed to stop calculating. There was considerable doubt that he was even a leisure-out. The most popular theory was that he had simply moved to the Zone many years ago because he preferred the company of fantasy freaks to that of normals. It was only theory, though. There were almost no hard facts on Joshua Long's background. Although he'd talk at length about any other subject under the sun, he was totally silent about his own past. Essentially, he was the preeminent Zone fixer. He put those who wanted implants or the more bizarre examples of plastic surgery in touch with not-too-particular surgeons. He arranged introductions between those who had large quantities of drugs and those who wanted them. He dealt in bootleg data and financed the manufacture of the illegally overpowered stim boxes. He converted black scrip into regular, and vice versa. Indeed, it was said that he had designed the whole black scrip system in the first place, but that was another of the Joshua Long rumors. Joshua Long was also a pack rat of grandiose proportions. He lived in a converted garage in the heart of the Zone that was filled with a lifetime's accumulation of junk and heavily protected by sentry robots. Aside from piles of unmarked crates that contained his diverse stock-in-trade, and four immobilized mid-twentieth-century Cadillacs that were swaddled in dust sheets and up on blocks and the kind of car for which any greez would give his right arm, he also possessed a huge and bizarrely eclectic art collection. From where Marlowe was sitting, he could see giant pop-art plastic fruit leaning against classic marble nudes. Plasma globes cast their eerie light over a stack of canvases that could have been Dutch masters or could have been fakes. Joshua Long also had one of the few remaining dogs on the planet, a brain-damaged Doberman that, according to yet another rumor, he had personally nursed through the canine mylosis plague. It was fortunate that he treated his extensive cellar more like his dog than his art collection. For Marlowe, he had selected a twenty-year-old single-malt scotch that he poured liberally. After what he had gone through that afternoon, Marlowe was more than grateful for it.

"You'd better fill in the blanks on Elias Stavers. I know he was the godfather of the space industry, but I'm hazy on the details. I haven't been taking too much notice of what's going on in the real world."

"It looks like you're going to have to start. There's life outside the Zone."

"I'm starting to realize that."

Joshua Long refilled their glasses. He was getting ready to perform again. He and Marlowe were sitting in a pair of aged but comfortable leather armchairs in what served Long for a living room. It was an L-shaped alcove. One arm of the L was a wall of packing cases; the other was a sophisticated, if mismatched, bank of electronics. An ancient silk parachute was spread out to form an artificial ceiling. The effect was not unlike sitting in the tent of a high-tech sheik.

"You want to hear the story from the start?"

"Sure."

"It's no exaggeration to say that Elias Stavers was the last of the greats, the Henry Ford or Howard Hughes of off-world development. He founded Stavers Industries around the turn of the century. It was when the national governments were starting to fail and the big corporations were taking over the space programs. Most people who jumped on the space boom went into hardware. The big deal was to put payloads into orbit, and that was the route that most entrepreneurs took. Stavers, on the other hand, realized that once the payloads were in orbit, once the space habitats and the moon colonies were established, once long-range ships were going out to Mars and to Jupiter's moons, there would be a massive need for software systems. Stavers surrounded himself with a brain pool of incredibly bright young people and went to work on predicting what those problems might be. Where he was particularly clever was that these systems were always created following the assumption that the need to move off-world would become increasingly pressing as conditions on Earth become intolerable. Even before the first big space stations were in place, Stavers had an available and interlocking system of software that could solve problems in a vast number of areas. Where Stavers had been even smarter was in the fact that his programs were designed to modify themselves as new data became available and that they were ultimately protected. Within what to some was an alarmingly short space of time, almost all off-world development was dependent on the Stavers Industries systems."

Joshua Long paused and sipped his scotch as if giving Marlowe time to absorb what he had said.

"Things went along okay until the time of the big consolidations. The two biggest corporations, IKG-Tokyo and RAMco, started to see off-world as their personal bailiwick. Starting with the smaller cowboy operations, they began mopping up the opposition. Takeover, merger, intimidation, plain skullduggery—they used every dirty trick until they virtually owned outer space, two supercorps sitting up there glaring at each other, just like the U.S. and the Soviets in the last century. The only fly in the ointment was Stavers. They tried everything to break him. They tried to duplicate his essential systems. They sent skaters in after his primary ice. They tried to break him on the markets, and I believe there were even a couple of attempts on his life. Stavers, however, always managed to stay one jump ahead of them. The world and, more especially, the off-world started to believe that he had the aura, that he was untouchable. I mean, there he was, this gadfly between the giants, each of them swatting at him but also each of them completely dependent on him. Are you following all this, Marlowe?"

Marlowe nodded. He was starting to feel dwarfed by the enormity of it all. "Yeah, but I rather wish I wasn't."

"Don't give up now, shamus."

"There's more?"

"One thing you have to remember is that during this time the supercorps were going through changes. As they had more and more of the early space stations, the doughnuts, up in orbit and more and more of their people in space, their thinking started to alter. They were leaving the planet. They began to take a decidedly superior attitude toward those of us who were left behind. They might one day return as our saviors, but no way were we their equals anymore. You know what it reminds me of?"

"What?"

"Have you ever seen the old 1930s movie, *Things to Come*?"

"Sure, Raymond Massey, Ralph Richardson."

"That's the one."

"What about it?"

"You remember the bit when after the world war and the plague, Ralph Richardson and his ragged-ass army are fighting a perpetual war with the guys who live over the hill, and then Raymond Massey shows up in his black suit, space helmet, and Art Deco plane and announces that this confederacy of airmen, Wings Over The World, is going to restore civilization?"

"It always struck me as steering mighty close to a fascist master-race theory."

"That's the way the supercorp people seem to be going. If not a master race, they certainly think they're a superior culture."

"Did Stavers go the same way?"

"I figure Stavers actually was superior but basically he didn't have the time. Two years ago, Elias Stavers dropped dead of ID4. For a man so driven, he seemed to find the time for a pretty advanced sex life, even by contemporary standards. That was the beginning of the end for Stavers Industries. Elias Jr., like so many of the sons of the great, was a lame, so much of a lame, in fact, that the old man cut him out of the succession. The family stock, which was by far the majority of the company, was split between the three grandchildren."

"Lawrence, Veronica, and Christine, the small family firm."

"Lawrence had by far the largest block of stock, but to offset this, Christine inherited key patents and some of the ultrasecret ice that was at the root of the key systems. She seems to have been the old man's favorite; maybe he thought he saw something of himself in her."

"She seems to have an advanced sex life, if nothing else."

"I wouldn't know about that."

Another rumor about Joshua Long was that he was totally asexual.

"Actually, that's about all I do know. From what you've said, it would seem that Veronica and Lawrence are about to sell out to either RAMco or IKG-Tokyo, and Christine doesn't want to. That would be the most logical reason for her hiding out among the vampires, although things are not always logical or even what they appear."

"You think that was really Veronica Stavers who came to see me?"

"I doubt it. She was probably an actress hired for the job. The question is, who hired her? You say that you felt you were being hosed with pheromones?"

"I don't know. At first I thought there was something going on."

"That was probably to keep you off balance. Did you ask her for any credentials?"

Marlowe shook his head ruefully. "Just money."

"You really don't know how to play this game, do you, Marlowe?"

That final remark kept coming back to him as he walked away from Joshua Long's warehouse home, along with the thought that there was no guarantee that anything would be as it appeared. Marlowe was in no doubt that he had blundered into an extremely dangerous game where the stakes were literally astronomical and he didn't even know if he had any cards.

It was dark when he came out of Joshua Long's. A sweaty, superheated fog swirled lazily through the streets of the Zone. He could taste the pollution even through his mask. It turned the buildings into looming black monoliths and the aimless crowds on the sidewalks into the walking dead. The traffic moved at a crawl. The hum of the cars' electric motors was muffled to an eerie silence; the cars themselves had become blind shapes, peering through the fog with dim yellow eyes. It would have been an ideal night for Jack the Ripper except that the temperature must have been pushing a hundred Fahrenheit. It was too hot for murder. At least Marlowe hoped it was too hot for murder. A figure swung through the air above his head—black, blue, gray, and a flash of yellow. Marlowe grunted. "Fucking Batman."

Comic-book superhero was one of the strangest fantasy cults in the whole of the Zone—dumb assholes dressing up in costume and swinging from forty-story windows or balconies on rubber ropes, scaring the hell out of the people on the ground. Marlowe's mood was rapidly deteriorating. The drugs had completely worn off, leaving him with a dry metallic feeling in his bones. The scotch that, back at Joshua Long's, had been like a warm angel caressing his jangled nerves was now just a headache.

It was only when he was quite close to his own apartment building that the thought hit. He blamed neural overload for making him so stupid. If anyone—the Stavers family, IKG-Tokyo, RAMco, or whoever—wanted to kill him, the smartest thing would be to wait around near his apartment and pop him when he came home. He looked around for a phone booth. The first and most obvious move would be to call his computer and have it scan the elevators, corridors, and approaches to his building. There was a booth at the end of the block. Marlowe scowled. With his luck, he'd find a Superman freak changing clothes in it.

As it turned out, the booth was empty. He stepped inside and keyed in his credit code. The Plexiglas sound shield lowered itself around him. He keyed in his own number. The screen showed static. When the snow cleared, instead of the loop of the cigarette burning in the ashtray, which he used as a video block when he either was out or didn't want to show himself, he got a flashing busy signal. With a sinking feeling, he rekeyed. It had to be a mistake. Again he got the busy signal. Now he was scared. Either there was someone in his apartment, using the phone, or someone had been in his apartment and left the phone off the hook. He stood there holding the handset and wondering what to do next. His first instinct was to run, to sleep in an overnight capsule and figure it all out in the morning. That was ridiculous, though. He couldn't just leave everything he had and vanish. He had to go back to the apartment. He thought about calling Veronica Stavers to see if she had any ideas. He decided against it. There was always the chance that she wanted him dead.

"Are you going to be in there all night?"

There was someone knocking on the sound shield. It was a redhead in black lace toreadors and a matching, low-cut top. There were blinking dialeds woven into the lace, and her mask made her face look as though it were cut from a single huge crystal. Normally, Marlowe would have grinned and maybe even flirted with a woman who looked like that, but the fear of death left no room for casual lust. He hung up. The sound shield lifted.

"It's all yours, lady."

He was going back to the apartment. He couldn't dedicate the rest of his life to hiding from invisible assassins. He was going back, and if anyone was there, God help them.

When he reached the apartment building, he stood on the corner for a full five minutes until he was sure that there was no one lurking in the lobby. Even then, he didn't use the front entrance. He walked around the back and climbed the steel steps beside the bay where the garbage trucks loaded up. He peeled off his mask so his vision wouldn't be obscured and almost gagged as the stench of the garbage bay hit him. He unsealed his coat and took out the Reaper, then used his card on the door leading to the corridors that ran through the bowels of the building. With the gun at high port, he edged his way carefully toward the subbasement parking lot.

When he reached the parking lot, he moved through the shadows until he could see the Buick. Nobody appeared to be watching it, and he moved on. His next stop was the elevator. He rode it to the floor immediately below his own and then walked slowly up the fire stairs. He paused for almost a minute before he stepped out into the corridor that led to the door of his apartment. Walking into a hail of bullets was no longer a romantic fantasy. It was real and vivid. Finally, he took a deep breath, screwed up his courage, and stuck his head out. There was nothing there. The corridor was empty. The only thing that he could hear was his heart pounding. He took the corridor one step at a time. Still nothing. He reached the door with its now rather pathetic sign. He gently pushed the door with his gun. The door wasn't locked. As he increased the pressure, the door swung open. There was only one light on, but that was enough to show that the place was a mess. Someone had conducted a crude search. That wasn't the worst, however. There was a figure sitting in his chair, behind his desk, seemingly waiting for him. He gripped the Reaper with both hands. His palms were sweating.

"Make a single move and I'll blow your head off."

The figure remained perfectly motionless. The light was behind it, so it was impossible for Marlowe to make out any features. He took three quick steps forward, then abruptly stopped. Now he could see. The figure was motionless because it was dead. He also knew who it was. He had seen the black leather mask so recently that there was no possibility of a mistake. It was Yorga's sidekick. There was one neat hole in the middle of his forehead. It looked as though it had been made by a laser. Temporarily blocking the ramifications of having a dead vampire in his apartment, his first thought was for Greenstreet. Where was his cat?

"Greenstreet, where the hell are you?"

There was no answering sound or movement. The cat could simply be hiding, terrified and furious at the ransack and murder in what he thought of as his apartment, or it could be worse. But even the death of a much loved cat couldn't be his first priority. There was a stiff in his swivel chair and something had to be done about it. He had two alternatives. He could call the police, or he could dump the body. The police didn't have too much sympathy for leisure-outs. The people in the Zone did contribute to the economy simply by consuming, but the cops had difficulty seeing it that way. Leisure-outs didn't do anything useful and therefore they didn't merit consideration. The cop mind-set was that the normals paid their wages and the normals got the protection. Even if he didn't wind up being charged with murder, any investigation into the death of the vampire could bury him in the precinct citadel for who knew how long, and a precinct citadel was scant protection against a halfway efficient corporate killer. He didn't want to think the thought, but he was going to have to dump the body.

The only thing going for him was that people would believe just about anything of a vampire. Whatever bizarre injury, the majority would think that it was self-inflicted, and the rest would assume that the vam had had it coming.

Lightning arced across half the sky and was immediately followed by a deafening clap of thunder. He moved quickly to the window. A violent nightstorm was about to rip. Down below, the streets would be emptying and the choppers, if not grounded, would be hugging the ground. As soon as the rain came down, the corpus delecti could go straight out of the window. After forty-five floors, the head should burst like a watermelon, obliterating all trace of the laser hole. With luck, the cops would think he'd been wall crawling and been caught by the storm. It wasn't that unusual. There was one window in the apartment on which he'd had the suicide proofing illegally removed. Screw the insurance company—it was good to be able to open the window without building security knowing about it. He began removing the bolts. The wind was already shrieking around the tower.

The rain hit like a hail of bullets. Swinging the window back and locking it open was like sticking his face into a hurricane. A small tornado swept a blizzard of paper through the already turned-over apartment, but there was nothing he could do about it. He wheeled the swivel chair with its payload of vampire to the window. He was soaked to the waist by the time he'd wrestled the body onto the sill. It was a relief to heave up on the ankles and let it go. It took all of his strength to fight the window shut. The thunder and lightning were practically continuous.

The downtown towers looked like illuminated tombstones. There had to be some gothic god looking out for him.

The papers in the room drifted to the floor, and Marlowe found that he was standing in a wet half circle. He pulled off his soaked trenchcoat and looked at the devastated apartment. This was a bitch. His life was supposed to be fantasy—not this mess. Pulling off his tie, he headed for the bathroom. As he pushed open the door, Greenstreet streaked out from behind the shower curtain. Marlowe tried to field him but missed. The cat seemed to have decided that, after the fact, panic was the best policy.

"Psycho!"

As Marlowe was stripping off his damp shirt, he noticed that the phone had been knocked over. He walked over to set it right. The moment he replaced the handset, the bell rang. Marlowe all but dropped it. His blood turned to ice. He wanted to throw the thing away as if it were a poisonous snake. It rang again. He struggled to get a grip. Greenstreet could afford the luxury of panic, but Marlowe couldn't. On the third ring, he thumbed off the visual and picked it up.

"Hello." His voice was tentatively neutral.

Something reptilian rasped in his ear. "So you are a vampire killer, Marlowe."

It was Yorga. How could he have found out so soon? The real killer must have told him. Marlowe couldn't think of another explanation. He was being framed.

"I don't know what you're talking about."

"Oh, yes, you do." The yes came over like a snake hiss. "Renfield is sitting in your apartment with a hole through his head."

"He isn't."

"I'm coming for you, Marlowe."

"You're making a mistake. I'm being set up."

"I'm coming to kill you, Marlowe."

Yorga hung up. The sound was like the soft click of doom.

Marlowe pulled a bag from a closet and started stuffing a few essentials into it. The storm was still raging outside. Surely the vampires wouldn't be there until it had blown itself out. He collected his drugs and the bottle of booze from his desk. He dug out all the remaining ammunition he had for the Reaper. He shivered as he pulled on his wet trench coat. All that was left was to take care of Greenstreet, who had regained his composure and was sniffing at the vampire blood that was soaking into the rug. For god's sake, don't lick it, Marlowe thought, I'll probably throw up.

There were three neighbors who would take in the cat. Cleopatra, Oscar, and the Pink Fuzzy Bunnies from Hell. He'd try Cleopatra. Oscar was too flaky to care for the animal, and although the Fuzzy Bunnies meant well, they were simply too unpredictable. He picked up Greenstreet, who complained bitterly.

"You're going to have to go visiting for a while. It can't be helped. I'm in a bunch of trouble."

He didn't specify how long a while might be. It was something that he didn't want to think about. For the moment, he was concentrating on going. He took a final look around the apartment and shut off the power. Bag in one hand and cat in the other, he let himself out. The door locked itself behind him. He walked on down the corridor and touched Cleopatra's buzzer. Let her be home, he prayed. She was.

"Hi, Marlowe, what's happening in the forties?"

"Can you look after Greenstreet for a week or so?"

Cleopatra took the cat and held him up. Greenstreet purred.

"Sure. No problem. Me and Greenstreet get along like a house on fire."

Cleopatra was over six feet tall and lived in mid-twentieth-century afro. Her hair was a perfect sphere that extended well beyond her broad, body-builder shoulders. She was dressed in a loose-fitting dashiki.

"You want to come in?"

"No, I don't have the time."

"Something wrong?"

"Yeah, life suddenly got a bit real."

"Well, I'll take care of this guy, and you take care of yourself."

"I'll call you when I can."

"I'll be here."

"If you don't hear from me, call Joshua Long."

"You're in that much trouble?"

"Maybe. You've got Long's number?"

"I've got it."

Marlowe fondled Greenstreet. "I'd better get going."

"Marlowe . . ."

"Yeah?"

"Take care of yourself."

"I'll do my best."

She closed the door. He listened to the bolts drop. There was a terrible finality about the sound. For the first time, he realized just how alone he was. He took a deep breath and headed for the elevator.

The shirakin hit the wall directly beside his head. One of its star points stuck hard into the plaster and lodged there, vibrating. One of the vampires that he'd seen in The Bat Cave—the male with the high white hair—was at the other end of the corridor. He hissed at Marlowe, baring his fangs as he slowly raised his arm to launch another of the killing stars. He seemed to have no conception that Marlowe could present any kind of threat. Marlowe threw himself flat, ripping the Reaper from its holster. He didn't bother to aim. He let go with a blast of seven-gauge from the gun's lower barrel. It caught the vampire in the stomach, lifting him off the ground and throwing him backward. Blood was spattered all over the wall. One of the Pink Fuzzy Bunnies from Hell opened the door to their apartment but quickly slammed it again. The cops could arrive at any time. Building security was probably on its way.

There were footfalls behind him. Marlowe swiveled. There was a second vampire, one that he didn't recognize, coming from the other direction, waving a pair of butterfly knives. Marlowe fired again. This blast was less accurate. It took the vampire in the shoulder and he went down screaming.

"Scumsuck! You shot me!"

Marlowe was on his feet and running for the elevator.

After what seemed like an eternity, the doors slid open. Fortunately, the elevator was empty. He flopped against the wall. An unpleasant thought struck him: the two vampires hadn't been wet. They must have already been in the building when the storm started. Yorga could even have called him from inside the building. If that was the case, they were playing with him.

The elevator was slowing to the forty-second floor. Marlowe backed up into a corner with his gun at the ready. The elevator stopped and the doors opened. There was a shriek, and a blue-skinned vampire stabbed at him with a telescope lance. The seven-gauge was very loud in the enclosed space. The vampire took it in the face. Blue skin turned red. The doors closed. Marlowe discovered that he was shaking. Now that he'd killed two, they'd never let up on him. The elevator went straight down. It didn't stop until the nineteenth floor, where Marlowe almost shot a pair of middle-aged leather lesbians who quickly decided to take another car. It didn't stop again until the lobby. Marlowe flattened himself against the wall. The doors slid open, and to his amazement nothing happened. Then he noticed the two building guards. One lay facedown on the lobby floor. The other was sprawled across a couch, some kind of steel shaft sticking out of the middle of his forehead. Marlowe had never seen such an expression of total confusion. He quickly hit the touch for the underground car park. If he could just get to the Buick, he'd have it made. He was sure that he could outdrive any vampire. The trouble was that the car park undoubtedly had to be where they'd be waiting for him. If he were them, he'd be lying in wait for him, hidden between the cars. The semidarkness of the parking lot was an ideal backdrop for vampire murder.

The elevator stopped. The doors opened yet again. Marlowe stood very still. There was silence. They had to be out there waiting for him, waiting for the mouse to come out of its hole and run. The unfortunate truth was that there was no other way. He tensed. There was no putting it off. He charged out of the elevator, firing as he went. When he reached the nearest car, he rolled under it. Someone sprayed the area with a wild burst from some kind of burp gun. The muzzle flashes were over on the left. It produced an orgy of breaking glass and stopped. The echoes flashed from support column to support column and bounced down from the concrete ceiling. Marlowe crawled between parked cars. Fortunately, the Buick was not too far away. He risked straightening. Something was swooping down at him—a vampire on a rubber rope, cape trailing, swinging a long leaf-bladed knife like a ghoulish Errol Flynn. Marlowe picked him off in one shot. The vampire shrieked, and its arms and legs windmilled. It crashed into the Plexiglas canopy of a reproduction '22 Aston Martin. The burp gun opened up again. Marlowe was sprinting. Aisle 12, Bay 7. He fired at where the muzzle flashes had been as he turned the corner of a row of cars. The Buick was seven cars down. He was running blind, praying that he wouldn't be shot in the back on this last lap. And then he opened his eyes.

The Buick wasn't there.

Marlowe halted. Vampires were coming out from all over. There were a lot of them. Lit from behind by headlamps, the leaders cast long, dramatic shadows. Marlowe didn't even bother to fire. It was now just a matter of how many he got before they got him. Vampire vengeance contained a good measure of Russian roulette. Marlowe thought about shooting himself, but he just couldn't do it. Suddenly, there was a scream of tires from one of the exits. It was the Buick, running backward at high speed. It broke through the line of vampires, scattering them left and right, and screamed up beside Marlowe. The back door opened.

"Get in, you idiot!"

Hands dragged Marlowe inside. The door slammed and the car shot forward with a scream of tires. Marlowe looked at his benefactors. Christine Stavers was in the backseat. Carmila, the vampire girl from the cage, was driving.

"What the hell is going on?" Marlowe demanded.

"We've been waiting for you."

"You almost waited too long."

"I had to see if you could handle yourself, if you'd be any use to me."

"How did you get my car?"

The answer came from the front seat. "You think I can't hot-wire an electric car?"

FOUR

THE SIGN ON THE FREEWAY READ "EXIT 40—MULberry Hills." Beneath it, in smaller letters: "Security Cordoned." They were heading into dome country, where the big money sheltered behind their security systems. The two-lane exit road ran between a pair of low, landscaped hills. Beyond the hills, the scene reminded Marlowe of a luxury moonscape. The road passed one large, softly lit dome and then ran on across velvety-dark park land dotted with its own discreet lamp standards, to a cluster of three more, slightly smaller structures that were arranged like a clover leaf. There was probably an all-weather golf course hidden out there somewhere.

Christine Stavers glanced at Marlowe. "This is the family estate."

"All of it?"

"No, just the big dome. The triple belongs to the De Ryskes."

"The bankers."

"They have to live somewhere."

Although tastefully low-profile, security was as tight as a drum in this up-market suburb. In front of the large dome there was an open space that was surrounded by an all but invisible zap field. The only way to reach it was by a raised ramp. The ramp wound through a complex mass relief, an original Doja, that would efficiently muffle a car-bomb blast.

"Major art as property protection?"

"My grandfather thought that it was a cultural breakthrough. He and Doja used to get drunk on sake together. Before Doja killed himself, that is."

At the end of the ramp there was a guard post disguised as a miniature mesa. The guards were already out and waiting for them, bullnecked brutes in tailored black pajamas. They were probably North Koreans and they didn't seem to like the look of the Buick. Carmila brought the car to a stop. A guard peered through the driver's window. There were three in all and they all wore Yamaha wrist lasers. It was a safe bet that a couple of heavy machine guns were concealed nearby.

"Please identify yourselves." He was North Korean and his English was perfect.

Marlowe glanced back at Christine Stavers. "You better square this."

She leaned forward. "Don't you know me?"

"Please identify yourselves."

"I'm Christine Stavers, goddamn it."

"I'm sorry, Miss Stavers. We have never personally met. I have only just been transferred here. I'll have to print you."

"All right, all right, just make it fast. Give me the printer."

The guard passed a portable printer through the open window. The light came on and Christine placed her index finger on the plate. The print immediately got the green light. The guard, however, wasn't quite finished.

"Who are these people?"

"They're with me, that's all you need to know."

"Very well, Miss Stavers, but there will be a mandatory pro-tem insurance adjustment."

"Whatever."

"There's one more thing, Miss Stavers."

"I realize you're doing this by the book, but please hurry it up."

The guard looked at Carmila and Marlowe. "You acknowledge that you enter and remain here at your own risk?"

Carmila giggled. Marlowe sighed.

"We acknowledge."

The guard nodded. "You want me to take the car down to the garage?"

"Please."

As he stepped out of the Buick, Marlowe noticed, not without some concern, that there was a long, ugly scratch across two of the door panels. The storm had blown itself out and the night was unnaturally clear. Here on the outskirts of the city pall, it was possible to see three or four stars as he followed Christine Stavers and Carmila toward the main temperature lock.

The interior of the dome was close to paradise, a paradise in the neo-nissan mode, a pueblo of advanced geometry that seemed designed to dazzle the beholder. Relieved of the demands of keeping out the weather, the architects had been free to indulge their wildest fantasies. Plants played a major part. The superrich liked to have life vibrating around them. Marlowe supposed that it was a psychological protection against the abundance of decay outside. In what could only be an approximation of a main entrance hall, there were no less than a half-dozen large trees, each with its complement of exotic, decorative birds. Taken as a whole, they gave the place the air of a baronial forest. A Henry Moore nestled in a luxuriant bed of rhododendrons. A lot of materials not usually associated with building had been employed in the construction. Spaces were divided by tapestries or long, flowing lengths of silk that billowed like the sails on a ship. A staircase in the ultimately grand manner, which swept up to the higher levels of the free-form structure, was made entirely from artificial crystal. Water flowed everywhere, in falls and streams and fountains and vertical expanses like sheets of polished glass.

"You suckers sure know how to live."

A miniature deer was drinking from a circular pool.

"Is that a real deer or a synthipet?"

"A real deer, of course."

Marlowe stuck his hands deep in the pockets of his trenchcoat, determined not to be awed by the overwhelming display of wealth. "Now we're here, what are we supposed to do? Do you intend telling me what's going on?''

''Be thankful you're safe from the vampires.''

''I'm wondering what's going to be after me next.''

''I figured we could relax a little and consider our options.''

''What about your brother and sister? Are they here?''

''They rarely come here. It reminds them too much of my grandfather. We won't be bothered.''

He and Carmila were following Christine into a kind of tunnel. The interior softly shimmered as they entered.

''Where are we going?''

She answered as if it were the most natural thing in the world. ''The Roman baths.''

''Roman baths?''

''That's what I said.''

Marlowe thought of his malfunctioning shower. ''You're kidding.''

''You don't have to kid in our income bracket.''

The Roman baths were a sunken area at the end of a flight of pink and black marble stairs. A long, narrow, rectangular pool was surrounded on three sides by a colonnade in the same material and color scheme. The walls were covered in silver-inlaid erotic frescoes in the classic manner. Between the pillars, there were ornamental benches and tables. A JOE bartender squatted in among them, lights blinking sadly, waiting for someone to ask it for something. Ambient sound harmonized with the natural noise of the water as a black swan paddled superciliously at the far end of the pool.

''That's a synthipet. Real swans shit too much.''

''It looks like a set for an orgy.''

''It has been.''

For Marlowe, descending into the baths was like walking into a trench of perfumed humidity. There were wisps of steam rising from the surface of the water. He didn't see the attraction. There was more than enough humidity where he came from. He took off his hat and trenchcoat and laid them on a bench. To his surprise, Christine Stavers started peeling off her black cat suit. She seemed to have favored a ninja look for her slumming with the vampires, or maybe that was just for the burglary and auto theft she'd been engaged in just before rescuing him. Once naked, she dived into the pool. Marlowe searched for a cigarette. He didn't have any. Carmila was also undressing.

"I didn't know we were going to a beach party."

"Take your clothes off, Marlowe, and get in the water. Caligula planned mass murder in places like this."

"I don't doubt it."

"If you're modest, there's a pile of towels over there."

Black turkish towels lay in a folded pile on one of the ornamental tables. Marlowe still hesitated. It wasn't that he was a prude. The reason he disliked being naked was that there were simply no references. Nobody did naked in the forties. It was as if he took off his personality with his clothes. Peer pressure and the fact that he was sweating finally got the better of him. He pulled off his tie. Carmila was now out of her complicated vampire costume. She was as strange out of her clothes as she was in them. He body was skinny to the point of desperation, mausoleum pale, and it carried more than its fair share of minor scars. A tattooed demon suckled on one tiny breast. She tied back her long, straight black hair. As she turned to dive into the pool, it became plain that she had recently been beaten, probably with a thin whip.

Marlowe had to admit that the warm water felt good. He paddled over to the JOE bartender robot.

"Hey, JOE, can you pour me a John Powers without electrocuting me?"

JOE trundled forward. "Of course, sir."

"Real or synth?"

"I carry real John Powers. All popular brands."

"How about cigarettes? You have any of those?"

"Cigarettes are illegal, sir. And besides, you can't smoke them when you're in the pool."

Damn robot logic.

"But do you have any?"

"I can get you some from elsewhere in the house, sir. What brand?"

"Zimbabwe Pall Mall."

"I'll get some as soon as I've poured the drinks."

With a drink in his hand and his elbows propped on

the edge of the pool, Marlowe felt ready to confront Christine Stavers. "I think it's high time we had a talk."

"You want to know why all these people keep trying to kill you?"

"It's an understandable curiosity."

"They want to do a lot worse to me."

"That's hardly my problem."

"It is now."

Marlowe sipped his drink. "Let me run by what you've already told me."

"Be my guest."

"So, as I understand it, a woman who tells me that she's your sister, but probably isn't, hires me to find you because there's a problem with the modest family business. The first thing you know about this is when I walk into The Bat Cave looking for you. You're hiding out there, and Yorga doesn't say anything because you're handing him and his ghouls large packages of money."

"You get the best action when you act transactional."

"Then some guys in a big black hydro burner try to run me down and I get inquisitive. The first thing I discover is that the modest family business has the corner on orbital system data and that the supercorps are looking to finally swallow you whole. The second thing I learn is that you're the only thing that stands between them and merger."

"I'm a very unfortunate young woman."

Marlowe looked around the Roman baths. "So it seems."

Christine dived under the water. Marlowe waited for her to break surface. When she did, he resumed.

"While I become the moving target, you decide to find out all about me by breaking into my place, you and her and the other one."

Carmila supplied the name. "Renfield."

Christine trod water. "Actually, I was pretty certain what you were. You'd be a wild long shot. The far end of some probability curve must have figured you might do better in the Zone than their pros in gray suits. RAMco and IKG have whole departments for that kind of lateral thinktanking. If they didn't hire you, my family did. Staverses have thinktanks, too. Someone intended to tail you in the hope you'd lead them to me. It was all really the same in the end. They all want my inheritance. I only broke into your place for confirmation and to find out if you'd be useful."

Carmila picked up the story. "Renfield was the best at B&E. He did the locks and went in solo to see if all was suitable while we waited. He was gone a long time, and then these three charcoal-gray norms come walking out. We go in and find Renfield dead. The only explanation is that they were corp killers looking for you and that they iced Renfield by mistake. We decide to get the hell out of there. Take your car. Next thing, Yorga's children of the night are all over the building, looking to kill you. We take off, except she decides to go back and save your ass."

"That was good of her."

Christine smiled. "It was, wasn't it?"

"So answer me the big-ticket question."

"Why should a giant corporation be bothering to kill you?"

"That's the one."

"I don't want to hurt your pride, Marlowe, but you're just a loose end. You could be an embarrassment, and embarrassments are always eliminated."

Marlowe frowned. "Are you telling me I'm as good as dead?"

"You're okay so far, aren't you?"

"There are jokes about that."

Christine laughed. "Stick with me, Marlowe, and we'll all get out of the woods."

"You reckon?"

"It's your best chance."

"I guess it is." He turned his attention to Carmila. "I've got a question for you, too. How come you went with her? Why didn't you stay with Yorga?"

Carmila was hauling herself out of the water. "The constant punishment became tedious."

There was an ice-water whirlpool at the end of the heated pool. Carmila walked over and lowered herself into it. Christine also climbed out of the pool. She stood on the edge looking down at him. He had seen her naked on video, but there had been vampires all over her. It'd done her less than full justice. She really had a magnificent body. There was also a hardness about her that came through as mere petulance on the video or the hologram.

"I think there's something that I should explain to you, Marlowe. Inheriting power is very different from just inheriting wealth." She wrapped herself in a turkish towel. "My grandfather taught me all about power. Neither my brother nor sister were interested. All they think about is the money, the short term. They can't see what our family really has. They are stupid, pathetic, overgrown rich kids. They have no grasp of the big picture. That's why they're so happy to sell everything my grandfather built to the Big Two."

"And you're not?"

"Of course I'm not. I'm the one with my grandfather's DNA. I have his blood in my veins and I have his vision. He knew that I was the only one who would continue that vision and that's why he left me the key patents and access codes. He trusted me with the very heart of his empire. I received the power, and it's no exaggeration to say that no one can make a move in space without my cooperation. For years, my grandfather fought the corps off his systems and prevented them from carving up off-world development between them. I'm going to keep Stavers Industries going and I'm going to keep the fight going. You could say that I have a sacred duty. I'm going to maintain that power. My grandfather put a lock on the future and I don't intend to let it go without a struggle."

Marlowe had never encountered a woman who, naked except for a turkish towel, talked about sacred duty and fighting the supercorporations. "Isn't it something of an uneven match?"

"My grandfather always played against the odds and he was always able to outthink them."

"And you think you're as good as your grandfather?"

"We shall see, won't we?"

"I don't want to sound like a doubter, but so far I'm the one who's getting shot at in this picture and I don't have any vision except for a long and healthy life."

"With all due respect, Marlowe, that's hardly my first priority."

"I kind of gathered that, but let's look at it another

way. If they're so all-fired to take me off the board, and I'm only a goddamn pawn, they're going to make damn sure they grease you. Surely, with you out of the way, your loving brother and sister would have a clear field to sell Stavers Industries to the highest bidder."

"No."

"No?"

"The one thing they're not going to do is to kill me."

Marlowe hauled himself out of the pool. He got himself a towel. JOE had returned with his cigarettes. He lit one and inhaled gratefully. "I wish I shared your optimism."

"It isn't optimism, Marlowe. I've made sure that they won't do that."

"You have?"

"Do you know what a dead-hand binder is in Swiss law?"

"Swiss law isn't exactly my field."

"It was introduced in the twenty twenties for situations exactly like this. You know what the Swiss are like. When an heir suspects that he or she is going to be murdered for an inheritance, it is possible to file a motion in Swiss civil court that, in the event of that heir's untimely death, the inheritance will remain frozen for ten years. Nobody can touch it. Not even RAMco can buck a Swiss court."

"Doesn't that put you in the clear?"

"Murder isn't the only thing that I have to worry about. They can do worse than that."

"They can?"

"They can break my mind. It wouldn't take more than a few hours of drugs and cortical stim. They could have me so zombied that I'd give them anything. They have departments for that, too. Afterwards, I'd be a vegetable."

"And how are you going to stop them doing that?"

"I have a plan."

"Are you going to tell me about it?"

"Not yet. I still don't know if I can absolutely trust you. You could be a plant."

"I'm not a plant, goddamn it."

"I'm assuming you're not, but that doesn't mean I have

to tell you everything. All you need to know is that it'll be my grandfather's favorite defense—the wipeblock."

"What's the wipeblock?"

"I'll tell you when it's time for you to know."

That seemed to be the end of it. Christine Stavers walked over to where Carmila was still in the ice-water whirlpool.

"What the hell are you still doing in there?"

"Mortification of the flesh."

"You'll freeze to death."

"No I won't, and besides, I'm about to get out."

"You're psychotic."

"That's why you love me."

Marlowe beckoned to JOE for another drink. The situation became more insane by the moment. He tried to keep his thoughts on a surface level. The drugs that he'd taken were wearing off. He hadn't slept for almost two days and he hadn't eaten in god knows how long. He had to stop thinking about corporate warfare and address these immediate problems.

"Hey, Christine. I don't want to cause any trouble, but I could really use a meal and a bed, in that order."

Christine looked up from rubbing down Carmila, who was now out of the ice water and lying facedown on a bench. "It shouldn't be any trouble. There aren't human servants anymore, but the kitchen is fully automated. It should be able to help you." She nuzzled at Carmila's ear. "Do you want to eat something?"

The affectionate gesture surprised Marlowe. It was hard to imagine this skinny vampire and meglo trillionaire as a sexual item, but he knew all too well that anything was possible. Carmila rolled over and shook her head.

"I try to eat as little as possible. I would like a cigar, though."

"Marlowe, why don't you go to the kitchen. Just ask and it will do what it can. It's all on-line."

"You keep the whole place on-line, even when you're not here. Isn't that a terrible waste of energy?"

"Yes, but we can afford it. Besides, the guards have to eat."

"So where's this kitchen?"

"You go up the marble stairs, along the kinetic tunnel, make a right, down the corridor and second left. You can't miss it."

The kitchen was larger than Marlowe's apartment and more than a little intimidating. With its gleaming chrome, steel, and black glass, it looked more suited to surgical procedure or space battle than to the preparation of food. The bank of spotless, fully integrated, and somehow aloof electronics gave the impression that it didn't care too much about the needs of human beings. He felt a little absurd in his shirt, pants, and bare feet.

"Can you do something for me, please?"

"If it is within my capabilities, sir."

"I'd like something to eat."

"Shall I show you a menu?"

"That would be a good idea."

A wall screen lit up, displaying a very comprehensive menu. The emphasis seemed to be on Anglo cuisine.

"This is the fast menu. Everything listed is available through microwave and will be ready in minutes. If you require natural cooking or something more elaborate, it will take longer."

"This menu will do fine."

He ran his eye down the list. "Steak and kidney pie, mashed potato, and carrots."

"Wine, sir?"

"A cold beer would be good."

"You will find beer in the manual refrigerator on the right. Your food will be ready when you hear the microwave chime."

Marlowe ate at a Lucite-topped table. Even though the food was precooked, deep frozen, and microwaved, it was a great deal better than most of what he normally lived on in the Zone.

"I could get used to this."

"Were you talking to me, sir?"

"No, I'm sorry, I was talking to myself."

Why was he apologizing to a kitchen? He must be getting punchy. The moment he laid his fork down, he found that he was yawning. He had half expected that Christine and Carmila would join him, but they hadn't showed. He still didn't know where he was going to sleep, and clean sheets seemed overwhelmingly appealing. He decided to go back to the Roman baths. He was starting down the marble stairs when he thought he heard voices. One of them belonged to a man. He stopped. Was it a guard making a round of inspection? He didn't think that the North Koreans came inside the house, and even if they did, what in hell was one doing in the Roman baths? Was Christine up to something weird? Without shoes, he could move almost soundlessly. He eased down a few steps. The male voice came again.

"I don't think there's any point in prolonging this. We should do it, and do it now."

There was a curse and then Carmila shrieked.

"Why don't we dispose of this one now?" The strange woman's voice had an angry tone. Maybe Carmila had bitten her.

It had to be trouble—and his gun was still down beside the pool with the rest of his clothes. Being tired was no excuse for being stupid. There had been no guarantee that he'd be safe in this luxury bubble.

The man's voice came again. "We have to find the leisure-out. We can't have him running around loose."

They knew he was there. He started to slowly back up the steps. Could he get to the car?

"So you must be Marlowe."

He slowly turned. A tall, thin man in the kind of black collarless twopiece and white drapeneck that was favored by corporate spooks was standing at the top of the stairs. He was pointing a recoilless Colt minimag at Marlowe's chest.

"Who's Marlowe? My name's Hopkins. I just got a ride with these two weird broads."

"Don't be cute, Marlowe."

"Cute?"

"Put your hands on your head and turn around."

"Whatever you say."

"Now walk down the steps."

Marlowe didn't argue with a minimag. He did exactly as he was told. There were three more armed, black-suited spooks beside the pool, plus a short, balding man in a lavender suit, a severely tailored woman who looked like an older, sour version of Christine, and a tall, graying man in formal pinstripe and dark glasses. Carmila was dressed, but Christine was still naked. Her arms were pinned behind her with black vinyl snaps. A spook was holding a gun to Carmila's head. The strange woman was nursing her wrist—Carmila had bitten her. Marlowe could only assume that the woman and the lavender suit were the sister and brother, Veronica and Lawrence Stavers. Veronica was definitely not the woman who had hired him to find Christine. There was nothing exciting about this woman. Her tan recsuit was like armor, and her face fell naturally into lines of dislike. It was strange that a woman who was so rich could look so bitter. The spook behind Marlowe pushed him toward the group.

"Here's Marlowe."

Lawrence Stavers rubbed his hands together nervously. "That's the set."

"We should take them upstairs. I can't work here." Even in the scented heat of the baths there was a graveyard chill in the older man's voice. Marlowe didn't want to think about his work.

Veronica Stavers was wrapping a handkerchief around her wrist. "I've probably got rabies."

"I could give you a shot."

"You'd love that, wouldn't you?"

"I am a doctor."

"Sure."

"If I'm going to do what you want, you'll have to tell me where I can work on her."

Veronica Stavers smiled unpleasantly at Christine. "I have an idea."

Lawrence looked even more nervous. He had clearly never been a match for his sisters. "What?"

"We'll take her up to the old man's meditation room. That would be poetic."

"You bitch!" Christine spat the word at her sister.

Veronica paused, then slapped her hard, open-handed, across the face. "You speak when you're spoken to from now on."

Christine clenched her teeth but didn't say anything. Carmila's eyes flashed, but she couldn't move. The gun was still pressed firmly against the side of her head.

"Shall we go?"

"What about the other two?"

"Bring them. They can watch."

They were marched up the marble steps with guns at their backs.

Located at the highest point of the structure, right under the apex of the dome, the meditation room resembled the onion-shaped top of a minaret. That style of architecture had to be a sop to the guilt that had been so rife after the nuking of Damascus and Istanbul. From the inside, the dome was even more like an onion. The circular floor was covered with a custom-made Persian carpet. The walls curved outward and then arced into the central peak. They were made from parallel strips of translucent, planiformed mica that split the light into soft rainbows. Exactly in the center of the space there was a huge, round couch, like a giant ottoman, some two meters in diameter and made from soft blue leather. A bench, covered in the same material, ran around the wall. One of the spooks directed Marlowe and Carmila toward it.

"Sit."

They sat.

"Move apart."

They moved apart.

The tall, graying man indicated that the spooks should remove the restraints on Christine's arms. As she stood massaging the circulation back into her wrists, he made a small, almost courtly half bow. He was like a well-mannered reptile.

"I am Dr. Raul Gossamer."

"I can't say I'm glad to meet you."

"Would you please lie down on the couch."

"Do I have any choice?"

"No."

Christine didn't struggle. With all the dignity that she could muster, she stretched out on the blue leather. One spook watched Marlowe and Carmila, while the others spread-eagled Christine and secured her wrists and ankles. There were a number of conveniently located metal rings around the base of the couch. Apparently Elias Stavers hadn't used the sofa solely for meditation. Marlowe glanced at Carmila. She was watching intently. She licked her lips with a small, pointed tongue. Marlowe wasn't sure if she was scared or just lapsing into voyeurism.

Gossamer turned to one of the spooks. "May I have my bag, please?"

One of the spooks handed Gossamer an old-fashioned black doctor's bag. He opened it and started laying out instruments on the couch beside Christine. His hands were pale and narrow with long, tapering fingers, and his movements were meticulous.

"I will start by administering a broad-spectrum cortical stimulant. That will open her mind to the more specific treatment." He ran an exploratory hand over her body. "She has already been fitted with two stim receptors that will suit our purpose admirably. One is in the back of her neck and one on the inner thigh." Gossamer talked as though he were addressing a class of medical students.

Christine turned her head and looked at her sister. "Do you know what you're doing?"

"We're facing reality, my dear. That's all. Since you refuse to accept the inevitable, it's being thrust upon you."

Lawrence was rubbing his hands again. "Should we really be doing this?"

Veronica shot him a look of pure contempt. "If we don't, the others will."

"She *is* our sister."

"She was also your lover once. Is seeing her naked giving you pangs?"

Marlowe raised a silent eyebrow. Shame and incest in the family.

"That's not fair. I'm just not sure it's right what we're doing."

"Shut up, Lawrence."

Dr. Gossamer was attaching stim leads to Christine. They ran back to a black heavy-duty power box. He turned it on. Christine let out a long-drawn sigh. Her eyes rolled back into her head and her pelvis jerked spasmodically.

"I'll run this for three minutes. After that, she'll be ready for the next phase."

Christine's hands were clenching and unclenching. She

was moaning softly. Her head had started rolling from side to side.

Veronica looked at her closely. "We don't want her so brain-damaged that she can't do what we want."

Gossamer turned from the stim box. His lips compressed. The expression was almost prim. "If you don't trust me to achieve the desired results, pay me off now and I'll discontinue the operation."

Marlowe was glad that he couldn't see Gossamer's eyes behind the dark glasses. He wondered how the man pictured himself. He probably didn't think of himself as a torturer. A man like that would have to live in a world of perpetual euphemism. He'd give himself a title—motivational adjuster or something like that. Christine was now straining against the restraints, twisting and writhing. Her movements were overtly sexual.

"Is she in pain?" Marlowe asked.

Gossamer shook his head. "Quite the reverse. She's in ecstasy."

The spooks had moved closer to the couch for a better look. They weren't paying too much attention to Marlowe and Carmila; they seemed completely absorbed in Christine's involuntary erotic display. Marlowe was surprised. He'd expected professionals to have greater detachment. Maybe Veronica and Lawrence had hired cut-price muscle. That would be in keeping with what he knew of their personalities. It was good to know that even trillionaires could be cheap. Or maybe it wasn't actually cheap, but just a lack of vision. That had to be the worst. To be stinking rich and dumb as shit. Gossamer was doing something to the controls on the stim box.

"I am now narrowing the focus to a tight, repeating endojolt."

Christine's back arched so violently that only her heels and the back of her head were touching the leather of the couch. Was Gossamer cut-price, too? If he was, there was the chance that she wouldn't live through all this. The spooks had moved in closer. They were all but drooling. They had to be the special of the week. Veronica and Lawrence must have bypassed the regular security department of Stavers Industries and gone shopping on their own. They didn't seem to have done particularly well. Marlowe wondered if there was any way that he could try something. Even if these guys were as low-rent as they seemed, he'd still need some kind of weapon. The Reaper was down in the Roman baths with the rest of his clothes. Out of the corner of his eye, he noticed that Carmila seemed to be doing something. She was still staring intently at Christine's arching body, but at the same time, her fingers were fiddling with the four or five studded belts that she wore, gunfighter style, around her narrow hips. At first he thought that it was just a nervous mannerism, then he saw that she'd actually detached one of the buckles and was drawing it slowly away from her body. From the way her hand moved, Marlowe guessed that the buckle was attached to something that was too fine for him to see, probably a length of ultrafine steel wire concealed inside the belt—loopwire. The ultrafine garrote was more of a naziboy weapon, but it wasn't unknown among vampires. Was she really going to jump one of the spooks?

She caught him looking at her and mouthed one silent word. "Gun."

She was going to loopwire one of the spooks and she expected him to catch the man's gun. It seemed like a good way to get himself killed. He wasn't a professional, just a good fantasist. He reminded himself that he'd taken care of the vampires okay, but it didn't help too much. About the only thing that made him consider the move was that he was almost certainly going to be killed anyway. Gossamer was turning off the stim. Christine collapsed like a deflated balloon.

"That's the three minutes. I will now give her ninety cc's of plasidrene before I proceed to the next stage."

He fitted a blue pressure bulb into a syrosol and touched the point to Christine's thigh. There was a faint hiss. Carmila seemed to take it as a signal. She moved with the speed of a striking snake. She spun the invisible wire in a miniature lasso, dropped it over the head of the nearest spook, and jerked hard. The man didn't make a sound, although his mouth formed a hideous, noiseless scream. His face turned bright red, going on blue, and his eyes bulged. His gun was in midair and coming in Marlowe's direction. That was the moment of truth for

Marlowe, and the world seemed to have gone into slow motion. He was reaching, arm outstretched like an outfielder going for an impossible home run. The gun was in his hand. He fumbled for a moment, working the butt into his palm and his finger around the trigger. The garroted spook had dropped to his knees. Carmila had her boot in the small of his back and was still hauling on the noose. The loopwire had bitten so deeply into the man's neck that Marlowe wondered if the head was going to come off. The other spooks were turning. One was bringing up his gun. Marlowe swung his own at arm's length.

"Freeze, you fuckers!"

Two spooks froze. Veronica and Lawrence froze. Even Gossamer froze with the syrosol still in his hand. The third spook, however, who was holding his gun but had it down at his side, simply laughed.

"You really think you've got the balls to kill anyone? This isn't the land of make-believe anymore."

He was thickset and florid with black hair combed into greasy waves. He looked like the kind who habitually equated presence of mind with testicles. He wouldn't have looked out of place hanging out with Al Capone. The way he slowly raised his machine pistol was a taunt. Marlowe didn't hesitate—and found it surprisingly easy. The bullet took the spook cleanly between the eyes. Blood and brains spattered Christine's body as he fell back on top of her. The other two twitched but didn't follow through. Marlowe must have struck them as considerably more determined than he felt.

"Anyone else want to try me?"

There were no more takers. Carmila had lowered the strangled spook to the ground and was slipping the noose out of the deep fold that it had cut into his neck. She had a feral expression on her face and was studying the group as if hoping for an excuse to wire another one.

"What do we do with these? Kill them?" she asked.

"I think two is enough," Marlowe replied.

"They would have killed us."

"We need to concentrate on getting out of here."

"I'm not going without Christine."

"We're taking Christine." He gestured to the others

with his gun. "Down on the floor, all of you. Face-down."

Once they'd done as they were told, Marlowe handed the dead man's gun to Carmila. "Cover them."

He had no doubt that she wouldn't hesitate to shoot anyone who moved. He picked up the other two guns and dropped them in each of his pants pockets, then he hauled the bloody spook off Christine and let him roll with a thud to the floor. She appeared to be out cold. He quickly pulled at the snaps that held her down on the circular sofa, but they refused to open. He realized that they must be voice-locked.

"Does anyone have the code to these things?"

Nobody answered. He took one of the guns from his pocket and held it against Lawrence's head.

"I'm not screwing around here."

Lawrence's eyes bugged. It was probably the first time his life had ever been threatened. His voice was suddenly an octave higher. "Tell him, for god's sake!"

The spooks on the floor still wanted to act macho. "Tell him to take a jump."

Marlowe walked over and slapped the man who had spoken hard across the side of the head with the barrel of the recoilless. "I'm in a hurry, damn it."

"Okay! Okay!"

"Out with it!"

The man spoke loud and clear. "If you don't give me the deeds to your ranch."

The snaps came open. Marlowe quickly used them on the wrists of their erstwhile captors. The only one he didn't pinion was Gossamer. "All locks please scramble," he said.

This time it was Veronica who protested. "Now we'll need an expert to get out of these things."

"That's the idea. Be grateful that we're letting you live."

"I'm going to get you, Marlowe, no matter what it costs."

"No doubt." He nudged Gossamer with his toe. "On your feet, doc."

Gossamer didn't argue. "What do want with me?"

Marlowe nodded to the prostrate Christine. "Do you

have something in your black bag to get her up and walking?''

''It'd be better to let her sleep.''

''I don't want to have to carry her out of here.''

''I can give her a shot, but she may not be coherent.''

''Just so long as she's mobile.''

This time the pressure bulb was yellow. For the first thirty seconds, nothing happened.

Marlowe bent over her. ''She isn't dead, is she?''

Her eyes suddenly opened. ''How you doing, big boy?''

At first he thought she was normal, then she tried to put her arms around his neck.

''Is that a pistol in your pocket, or are you just pleased to see me?''

Marlowe ducked away. He turned to Carmila. ''Help her. Get her dressed and ready to go.''

''Her clothes are still down by the pool.''

''So take her down there.''

Carmila led the raving Christine away. She was now babbling disjointed obscenities. Marlowe's next stop was Gossamer.

''Back on the floor, you.''

''You don't have to do anything to me. I'm the doctor.''

''Shut it, before I get angry.''

He caught up with Carmila and Christine in the Roman baths. Christine had moved on to Emily Dickinson, dredged from some back alley of her memory, but at least she was dressed and ambulatory. He put on the rest of his clothes.

''How do we get to the car?''

Carmila spread her hands. ''I don't have a clue.''

Christine broke away from Emily Dickinson and spoke in a perfectly rational voice. ''There is an elevator at the end of the kinetic tunnel. You take it to sub-basement three. The cars are there.''

She looked puzzled. ''I'm a little teapot, short and stout. Here's my handle, here's my spout.''

''Christ,'' Marlowe said. ''How long is this going to last for?''

''Who the hell knows? Maybe Gossamer damaged her

permanently. He could have done it out of spite or just plain ignorance.''

''Great.''

There were a number of cars in the dark and echoing underground garage. Marlowe started walking toward the Buick, but Carmila stopped dead and planted her hands on her hips.

''What do you think you're doing?''

''Getting in the car.''

''That electric heap?''

''It's my car.''

''Why not take that?'' She pointed across at a gleaming black monster on the other side of the garage. It was a thirty-eight Jensen Apollo, a hydro-burning, high-performance classic. ''It can hit three hundred kay and outrun anything.''

She was absolutely right—if one were on the run, it might as well be in one of the world's all-time greatest cars. It was just that he was so damned fond of his Buick.

''Maybe it's locked.''

It wasn't.

''Please secure all doors and body restraints.''

Marlowe hated talking cars. He'd drive the Jensen, but he'd never love it. He gunned the engine to drown its voice. Power vibrated through his feet. He glanced at Christine to see that she was okay, then eased the big black car into drive and headed for the exit ramp.

FIVE

"How is she back there? Still a little teapot?"

"Drive the car, Marlowe. She'll be okay. She's sleeping off Gossamer's cocktail."

"You sure she's not going to drop dead on us?"

Christine raised her head. "I'm . . . going . . . to . . . be . . . okay." Her speech was very slurred.

"I thought you were out cold."

"I . . . can . . . hear . . . you. It's . . . just . . . very hard to . . . do anything . . . about it."

"The question is, where are we supposed to be going? We can't go back to the city. The cops have to be looking for us by now."

"As far away . . . as . . . possible."

"Why don't you really drive this thing, Marlowe?" Carmila said. "I told you when we took it, it can do three hundred. Why crawl along at fifty like it was some piece of electric crap?"

"So what do I do? Burn up to two and a half and get even more police down on us?"

"Out here . . . we're . . . the law. Speed . . . is one of the . . . privileges of . . . power."

"She's right, Marlowe. All you have to do is hit the e-laner."

"You're starting to get on my nerves."

"Screw you, Marlowe. I saved your ass earlier."

"That part was okay. It's the subsequent backseat driving."

"It's not my fault you can't drive a real car."

Marlowe scowled and searched the instrument panel. The proximity warning sounded.

"Watch the truck!"

"Shit!" Marlowe spun the wheel. While looking for the e-laner, he'd all but rearended a truck. The Jensen politely inquired if Marlowe would like it to drive itself. Marlowe snapped at the car. "Just tell me where the e-laner is."

A display appeared in the lower half of the screen, pinpointing the position of the e-laner on the panel.

"As you will see, the Emergency Lane Override and Permit Transmission is the double-action toggle to the left of the Cabin Environment touches."

"Thank you."

Marlowe pulled the toggle out and up. A number of lights came to life on the instrument panel. The car wanted to know if it should take control.

"Let the car drive, Marlowe. It can go flat-out and we'll all feel a lot safer."

Marlowe touched the autodrive. Although he hated to admit it, he knew that he'd be out of his depth at three hundred kilometers an hour.

"Entrance to Emergency Lane in half a kilometer."

The car not only talked. It had a George Sanders, English accent.

"Why does your car sound like a butler in a movie?"

"How . . . the hell . . . should I know?"

The Jensen crossed the divider strip and turned into the e-lane. If the permit hadn't been transmitting, the divider strip would have shredded the car's tires. They were now in the specially surfaced private preserve of police, the military, paramedics, and the extremely rich.

"Counting to overdrive."

The overdrive cut in and the passengers were pushed back in their seats as the engine surged. The wide rear wheels were laying plastic and trailing smoke. The velometer hit 150K and went on climbing. It passed 200 and finally leveled out at 292. The landscape screamed by outside.

"Jesus!"

"Now this is what you call motoring," Carmila said happily.

They had left the enclaves of the superrich behind and were running on an elevated highway above the sprawl of the old suburbs. Marlowe rested his hands on the locked wheel and peered through the side window. The people in the inner cities thought they had it bad, but at least the cities were sectioned so the gunships were always around. Out here, the only safe places were the protected high rises that stood at regular intervals like geometric Christmas trees with their lights blazing. These were the homes of the low-rent normals and they towered luminously over the dark areas of one- and two-story tract houses. In these areas, the utilities were spasmodic and the policing minimal. This was where the marginal crowded together in decaying twentieth-century real estate and were preyed upon by the real lowlife. Somewhere in the distance, somebody's real estate was burning.

"There is a major intersection in two kilometers. The options are to continue on SH427 or to take the Axis Beltway to the city. The first exit on beltway is for McCarthy Boulevard and Walled Village."

Walled Village was well named. It was an executive fortress estate where middle management tolerated the good life behind guard walks and watchtowers. Marlowe shook his head. It was like the Middle Ages out here. He was very glad that they were running in the closed and monitored emergency lane. The outer, public lanes were all too prone to amateur roadblocks and booby traps. Kids, going to extremes with random vandalism, would haul huge blocks of concrete up onto the highway to waylay the unwary. Even at a modest, electric-car fifty, a head-on impact with one of those could be deadly. More serious, profit-motivated highway muggers would set crude, homemade landmines, detonate them under a car or a truck, and then rob what was left of the victims. Marlowe took his hands off the wheel and turned to the women in the back. He had too many problems of his own right now to worry about the abominable state of the nation.

"So what's it going to be?"

Christine had managed to sit up. "Stay on the . . . superhighway. They'll trace us if we go back . . . into the city."

"Speed we're traveling, four twenty-seven will have us in the badlands before we know it."

"Exactly."

"You actually want us to go into the badlands?"

"It's the hardest place for any corporation goons to come looking for us. They'd probably have to go shopping for . . ." She gave Marlowe a meaningful look. ". . . another specialist."

"Do you know what to expect in the badlands?"

"I think so."

Marlowe looked doubtful. "I don't know."

"Have you ever been in the badlands, Marlowe?"

"No, but I watch a hell of a lot of TV."

Even the lights of the high rises were behind them now. They were crossing a dark area of abandoned industry. The taller structures were silhouetted against the skyshine like the skeletons of picked-clean mechanical monsters. Here and there, isolated lights gleamed, but they were exceptions. These were places of dead shadows and rusting metal, where rats, cats, dog packs, and terminally bottom-rung subfolk scavenged the most awfully meager of livings. Marlowe shuddered and looked ahead through the windshield. He could do without the guilt that came naturally from sitting comfortably above it all in a fast, expensive car. They were approaching the Paul Reuben Bridge. The moon, pristine and white, had broken through the pattern of high, racing clouds. The bridge gleamed, looking white and incongruously new against the desolation all around it. The moonlight was also reflected from the slick oily surface of the river and softly illuminated the way in which the decay on the land seemed to stretch down and into the water, creeping along the collapsing piers and the hulks that rotted in the shallows.

There was life on the other side of the river. A vast chemical plant was bathed in soft, pale green floodlighting. The tall spiderweb stacks were festooned with tiny lights and had pulsing alarm clusters at their very tops.

At regular intervals, two of them belched gouts of emerald fire.

"And this ain't even the badlands yet."

"Badlands nothing. This is an Industrial Reclamation Area."

The badlands came soon enough. Warning lights flashed on the Jensen's instrument panel.

"We are entering an Underwriters Designated Own-risk Containment. All but third-party liability coverage is canceled on entry. Please confirm your intention to enter."

"Yeah, go right ahead into the badlands. Don't worry about us."

Marlowe couldn't remember how many times he had wondered how he'd achieved all of this. He felt so totally under the control of events that if it hadn't been for the fact that he was scared rigid, his situation would have been laughable.

"I mean, the badlands?"

"What?"

"Nothing. I was just thinking out loud."

He hit the Environment Report touch on the dash.

"The weather will remain fair with high cloud and a moderate wind from the southeast, although there is a possibility of precip later tomorrow afternoon. In the enclosure that we are about to enter, the toxins are within tolerable levels and there are no deviations from the standard picture of background radiation. No protective clothing is needed."

"That's a blessing."

The road described a downhill curve. Halfway through it, the sanitary strip came into sight. On this side of the area, the barrier was fairly minimal. In the middle of a hundred meters of plowed and floodlit dirt, a high chain-link fence was topped by a running fleur-de-lis of razor wire. On either side, the fence was reinforced with pits and concrete tank traps. The rationale for the containments and the fences around the badlands was that they prevented the spread of toxins and radioactive contamination. As with most rationales, though, this one was unashamedly transparent. Everyone knew that the real reason for the sanitary strips and the barriers was to keep in the people who had escaped into the areas during the reorganization and now couldn't get out. This was clearly demonstrated by the way in which the fences that bordered on the city and suburbs were little more than tokens, without watchtowers, patrols, or minefields, while on the other side, where the badlands bordered on the remaining farm country, there was a wall of steel to rival any European frontier. Few vagrants wanted to sneak back into the city. Most of them had fled from the city in the first place. Everyone, on the other hand, wanted to get to where the crops still grew and there was still food and work. On that edge, the guard towers were manned by Population Management troops, and PM Rhino gunships were constantly in the air. Without them, the vag gangs that roamed the badlands would stream into corn country, looting, raping, and burning. At least, that was the popular paranoia that kept the PM funded. Population Management had rapidly become the standard euphemism for applied brutality inflicted on the subfolk. Lest they forget that they were the world's unwanted, the PM was always there to remind them. Not content merely to hold the line, they ran raids into the containments to break up the larger vag gangs and harass the smaller ones with gas, sonic pounders, and Fleisher guns.

This particular containment, the largest in the east, was the elongated tract of land that had been downwind of the Salt River plant twin meltdown. The Salt River disaster had been a particularly bad one. When the containment vessel had gone, the spew of radioactive gas had produced a scar of third-degree contamination over 700 miles long. The destruction had been compounded by the DX plant virus that had followed the radiation, borne on the same winds. The vegetation that had survived the meltdown was largely wiped out by the epidemic. The containment was now a place of abandoned towns, dead, dry forest, and mutated grasslands.

Where the road intersected with the sanitary strip, it was crossed by what looked like a row of toll booths. The traffic in the public lanes had to slow to a halt and present ID for inspection. In the emergency lane, one was allowed to streak through unchecked. There was never any question about one's legitimacy and, best of all, no computer record was made of one's passing. It was likely, however, that someone or something would note a car like a Jensen heading into the badlands and file the fact.

"In this Containment, the integrity of the emergency strip cannot be counted on and we could encounter deliberately placed obstacles. I am therefore slowing down to fifty-five."

"It was nice while it lasted."

"Would you care to drive again?" the Jensen asked politely.

Christine was now fully awake. "I'd like to pull over and eat something. I'm starving."

"Did you have to wait until we were in the badlands?" Marlowe commented.

"The first priority was to put as much distance between us and whoever might be after us."

"But now that you feel you've got a bit of a jump on them, you're hungry?"

"It'll also be dawn soon. We should hole up somewhere. This car will attract too much attention driving around in daylight. Marlowe, ask the car if there's anywhere nearby where we could eat and sleep, a motel, or a truck stop—"

"I wish to hell you'd stop giving me orders like I was the help. It could get on my nerves."

"I fall into it naturally. It's one of the attributes of the spoiled brat."

"There is a Holiday Court in seventeen kilometers, after the High Tension Grove exit. It is attached to the parent corporation by a partial containment franchise. It holds an E7 security rating."

Carmila sniffed. "That's about as low as it goes, short of nothing. It means that broken-nose thugs in second-hand cop suits will club you stupid if they catch you drinking moonshine from a jar."

Marlowe turned and looked at her. "You've been in the badlands?"

"Where do you think vampires come from?"

"I don't believe you."

"I didn't expect you to."

Christine retained her air of command. "We'll try the Holiday Court."

As they drove farther into the badlands, Marlowe noticed that there was an increasing amount of graffiti scrawled on the highway signs. It hardly seemed a good omen.

The Holiday Court was built on the top of a small rise and surrounded by defenses a good deal more formidable than those they'd passed at the edge of the containment. The whole area was brightly floodlit. Outside of the wire there was a full-scale vagrant jungle, complete with dead vehicles, cannibalized containers, Styrofoam and cardboard shanties, cookfires, and teeming humanity.

Christine let out a long breath. "Sweet Jesus!"

"Seeing it for the first time?"

"So are you, Marlowe."

"At least I knew it was out here."

"Don't try and guilt-trip me, Marlowe. A leisure-out has no reason to get snotty with a billionaire."

The car wanted to know if Marlowe would like to drive. Marlowe took the wheel. Negotiating their way through the Holiday Court's defenses would allow him a certain distance from the two women in the back. He was feeling that it was hard to be on the run with two people who were so arrogantly certain that their acts were valid.

Carmila had been only partially right about the security. The guards did have flattened noses, but their uniforms were blue and gold tinsel—Ruritanian soldier suits, although the outfits had clearly been handed down through a long line of flunkies before they had come to rest at this last outpost. There was a line of them in front of the main gate. Despite their somewhat ludicrous appearance, they had to be taken seriously—there was nothing Student Prince about either the expressions on their faces or the Sterling burp guns hanging from their shoulders.

As the car approached the gate, the vags and hobos came out of the darkness and started closing in on it. They surrounded the Jensen like the living dead, peering through the smoked glass with dull, resentful eyes. When they pressed forward and started pawing at the windows with their grimy hands, Christine became alarmed.

"Marlowe, electrify the outside of the car."

"Lighten up. The windows are bulletproof, goddamn it."

"Electrify the damned car."

Marlowe angrily shook his head. "Forget it. I'm not going to zap these poor bastards."

He didn't have to. The security moved forward, snarling and swinging their clubs with an angry relish betraying that unique hatred that those just above the bottom feel for the ones who are already down there. The vags were driven back up the slopes on either side of the approach road. The Jensen was quickly waved ahead; Marlowe figured a car like that required no other credentials. The gates closed behind them, and outside, the security resumed their positions. Marlowe drove slowly under the rainbow arch and on toward the main complex of buildings.

The Holiday Court was an architectural leftover. It might well have been one of the last surviving examples of the plastic crystal craze, that unhappy marriage of Buckminster Fuller and the Snow Queen that had sprung up as gas stations and fast-food outlets right after the Titan landings. Three misshapen blue domes housed the main cafeteria facility. In their center, a cluster of jagged golden spars appeared to serve no function at all. Over to the left, a row of smaller domes around an equally misshapen, and now drained and derelict, pool played the role of motel cabins. Where the driveway turned off to the secured parking lot, a grove of dead, blackening trees stood forlornly casting long shadows, a reminder of what had once been mass fashion landscaping. There were no live trees in this area.

The car was checked in and immobilized, and Marlowe and the women were free to take care of their own needs. There had been a single heart-wrenching moment when a detector had discovered Marlowe's Reaper in the shoulder holster under his trenchcoat. But he learned immediately that for a fee and a tip, he could leave it with the parking-lot guard on promise of its return when he left. Carmila's more subtle weapons went unnoticed. As they walked to the largest of the domes, the air seemed fresh and clean. The moon was just visible above the glare of the floodlights.

Christine didn't seem interested in the night sky. "I've got credit in four different names, plus black and regular scrip. I think we should be okay. It'll be traced in the end, but we should be long gone before they can pinpoint us."

Carmila, on the other hand, was staring up at the moon. "I'm glad we're okay."

Christine flashed the vampire girl a strange look but otherwise didn't respond to the cryptic comment. Marlowe glanced at the two of them. He was too tired and preoccupied to try to figure out the parameters of their seemingly devoted hostility.

Right inside the main Lucite doors, a man in white-pan makeup and a black-and-yellow-checked suit was screaming angrily into the handset of a credit phone. "Listen, favorite angel, I don't give a fuck about the metaphysics. All I know is that six and one are seven and that's two too many."

Once upon a time, the Holiday Court must have been a fairly splendid place, judged by the standards of a franchised roadhouse. The high curved ceiling in the restaurant was set with sapphire optic panels shot with glowing gold filaments. Their shape followed the configurations of the irregular interlocking sections that made up the dome. Over the years, these must have dimmed or even had their power reduced. The colors had faded to a uniform, washed-out blue that made everyone in the place look as though he or she had been dead for a few days.

"God, it's like being inside a cheap piece of costume jewelry," Carmila commented.

Underfoot, the fitted, industrial carpet had probably started life as some shade of near beige with a name like cookie crumb. Now it was scuffed and worn to the color of mean average dirt. It had an adhesion that could only come from layers of ancient chewing gum. The most depressing thing about the place was the smell. The air was stiff with the odors of a generation's worth of superheated frying compound, microwaved soy, and hot tinfoil. Carmila looked appalled. "Do we have to stay here?"

Marlowe thought that her attitude seemed a little picky for a vampire. "You have a better idea?"

"No."

For a roadhouse in the badlands, the place was surprisingly crowded. Marlowe wouldn't have imagined that there would be so many people with credit and credentials moving through there, but he figured that they all probably had their reasons, just as he and the women did. There was a wide variety of style. Some were predictable: road obsessives who used the badlands and its lack of policing as an arena for their fantasies. Car cowboys in wide hats and leather vests eyed the more traditional Brando bikers and wondered about the chances of assignations in the bathrooms. A gaudy, old-fashioned jukebox glowed pink-magenta and purple in a wall niche on the other side of the room. It's speakers were pumping out a bizarre combination of Hank Williams, Johnny Cash, and Fex Oyeah, although a large number of the patrons chose to be wired into their own individual audio units. As far from the juke as possible, a family of joads, who had probably just fallen off the normal and hit the road with the last of their credit, sat miserably around a table wondering what to do next—the only thing that was certain in their lives was the lack of a way back. The two kids were hooked into a Williejohn, so at least they were quiet. Their mother monitored the dreamstate on the machine's small color screen. John and Willie rolled and romped through a bright plastic landscape that shimmered, dissolved, and folded in on itself in kiddywink hallucination. Marlowe wondered what would happen to the kids when the parents could no longer afford power packs. Kicking the only just-legal play machines could be rough on a child. Not as rough, though, as what they would face when the whole damn family became subfolk.

A group of boot-and-saddle truck jocks were taking turns in playing a lexilux machine. They looked up curiously as Marlowe and the two women walked in. For the first time, Marlowe realized that he and his companions weren't exactly inconspicuous. He'd been living in the Zone for too long. Out here, a man in a full forty trenchcoat and fedora, in the company of one young woman in complete vampire weeds and another who was only marginally more conservative with her halo of platinum hair and second-skin leather dress with silver buckles running up one side from a thigh-revealing slit skirt, had to be a cause for comment.

"Maybe we should find ourselves some new clothes. We kind of stand out the way we are."

Carmila sniffed. "What do you expect us to do? Rob a washing line?"

She obviously didn't want to be separated from her image. Marlowe could sympathize but also didn't feel that a look, no matter how carefully cultivated, was something to die for.

"Let's get something to eat and think about it later," he suggested.

There was a cafeteria-style counter, separated from the main restaurant by a Plexiglas divider. The Holiday Court food didn't look any better than it smelled.

"Are we supposed to eat this stuff?" Carmila asked.

"You don't have to, but there isn't much alternative," Marlowe replied.

Most of the food just lay there sweating and limp in the hot counter display trays. More was packed and racked, ready for the microwave. As nourishment, the food would probably suffice, although there was always the chance that it was tainted. The badlands didn't run to health inspectors, and a good deal of contaminated food was dumped there to be sold to either the desperate or the unsuspecting. As a taste treat, it left a lot to be desired. The shaping and coloring and chemical flavoring were so implausibly industrial that there was not even a pretense that it was anything other than soy, kelp, compacted crill, polyfiber, or bulked corn syrup. Carmila dove straight into the deep end with three helpings of turkey dogs and cranberry, and a couple of cans of Jolt. Christine was a little more fastidious. She elected to play it as safe as was possible with some rather dowdy fresh fruit and a carton of orange drink with the list of ingredients printed too small to read. She rubbed the fruit around in the bed of ice in which they were displayed.

"You can't be too careful."

Marlowe helped himself to a dish of soyjacks and doused them liberally with syrup. There wasn't much to be said for soyjacks except that they were honest. At the checkout, Christine paid with regular scrip. Marlowe glanced at her.

"Is the cash going to hold up?"

"For a while."

As they carried their trays to a table, a truck jock made a not terribly inventive suggestion as to what Carmila might do with the turkey dogs. Marlowe had expected her to either laugh off the obscenity or to counter it with one of her own. To his surprise, her face froze in a fleeting moment of absolute fury. In that first instant, Marlowe had a vision of her whipping out a razor and castrating the man. But her expression thawed and faded as quickly as it had come. She mastered the emotion and contented herself with a venomous hiss. Marlowe was reminded that he should never let himself relax totally around the vampire girl. Anger of that magnitude, no matter how brief, had to be fueled by a deep-seated psychosis. She was probably quite as crazy as Yorga or any of the others, and she might not be on his side forever.

When the meal was finished, Christine leaned close to the other two with an expression that seemed to say that she had made a decision. "I know what I'm going to do."

"You do?" Carmila was playing with the remains of her turkey dog. There was something catlike about the way she treated her food. She stabbed at it and pushed it around the plate as though she were pretending to torture it before she finally put it out of its misery by eating it. Marlowe realized that it was the first time he'd seen a vampire eat. He turned his attention to Christine.

"Is this the secret plan? Does that mean that you've finally decided to trust me?"

"Do you have to be quite so flippant?"

Carmila pointed a plastic fork at Marlowe. "Yeah, Marlowe, can't you take anything seriously?"

Marlowe looked around the restaurant. A brace of uniformed security were standing over the joad family, talking to the father. It was clearly one of those moments that happened only to the poor and drifting: either order something more or get out. From his gestures, the father seemed to be trying an emotional appeal. The security men were stone-faced. Marlowe sighed. There was always something to remind him that there but for the grace of the leisure-out program went he. "Isn't this serious enough to be going on with?" he replied.

The truck jocks still seemed to be talking about Carmila. They kept looking in her direction. Christine didn't seem to have noticed the attention that she and her companions were drawing. Maybe that was another product of great wealth, Marlowe thought. One expected people to stare.

She leaned even closer. "I've decided to use the wipe-block."

Marlowe realized that they had started to look like conspirators. "Should we really be having this conversation out here in public?"

Christine turned and for the first time saw the truck jocks. "You're probably right. Let's go and get ourselves a couple of rooms and talk there."

A surly reservation unit, one of the old-fashioned wall-panel models, gave them two cabins overlooking the dry pool. When Christine informed it that she was paying in cash, it became positively contemptuous and almost trapped her hand as she dropped the cash into the hopper.

"Who programs these things, or do they just get rude with age?" she said.

Marlowe grunted. "Probably someone who's scared shitless of losing his job and winding up out here. Putting personalities on clerical programs has got to be the last stop on the line. Insecurity makes people cruel."

As they headed for the row of cabins, Marlowe saw the joads for the last time. They were trailing across the parking lot toward a car that was loaded down with bundles and boxes and strapped-on furniture. A hard inner voice told him that he shouldn't feel sorry for them. They'd chosen the real path; they'd opted for fertility, family, and the good job. It wasn't his fault that they had let the system beat them, or that the system no longer gave second chances. Why should he feel guilty because he was lucky? There had been times when he would have liked to have had children.

The interior of the cabin was depressingly functional, a king-size bed with coin massage, a pair of suspension chairs, a wall-mounted TV, and an ironic mass-produced woodland landscape over the bed. A sliding panel opened on a minuscule bathroom.

"Christ, it's like a set for a suicide."

Christine stood in the middle of the floor and slowly turned. She looked uneasy. "I wish I could have this place swept for eavesdroppers."

Carmila grinned. "No problem."

She detached a small chrome box from her belt. It was about half the size of a cigarette pack. Marlowe had assumed that it was simply an ornament.

"You carry a sweeper around with you?"

"You don't know about vampires and electronics, do you?"

She skillfully swept the room. When she was through, she grinned at Christine. "It's clean. There's just the normal fire and theft monitors. There are points for a couple of listeners, but nothing's hooked to them."

Marlowe sat down on the bed. "So what's the wipeblock?"

The women took the two chairs. Christine looked very serious.

"The wipeblock was my grandfather's key technique for protecting his most secret and sensitive data. In very simple terms, when a section of crucial data suspected that its integrity was being violated, it immediately self-destructed."

"That seems a little wasteful."

"Of course it would be, if it were that simple, but obviously it isn't. A logic engine would be able to boot the self-destruct into a tilted mirror box."

"What's a tilted mirror box?"

"It's something that can image to infinity. In this case, it's an infinite cycle of violate, destruct, and resurrect. In an endless run of Zeno jumps, the data is always ahead of the prober by one position. That's not all, though. When the cycle starts to kick up into a Dworkin crescendo, as it's programmed to do, a cadence is created that will eventually feed back all over whatever is causing the violation and, if it persists, destroy it."

Marlowe shook his head. "I don't know what the hell you're talking about."

"Most people don't. It's complicated."

Carmila folded her legs into the chair. "It's not that complicated. What she's saying is that a wipeblock's something that self-destructs if you mess with it."

"That's putting it crudely."

"But there's a way out by which it can not only re-image itself on the halfshell but also rehose the shit back where it came from."

Christine half smiled. Her accent changed to an approximation of Carmila's hiss. "Reranch the optimess."

Carmila grinned, showing sharp little teeth. "Verisimilitude."

Marlowe was bemused. High cybercrat met vam speak and, to his amazement, mingled. He had been hiding in 1948 for too long. All he could do was try to be practical. "So, if I've got this right, you want to get to one of these logic engines and set up this protection."

"I'm afraid it's not as easy as that. The very basic and most secret data was stimloaded directly into my brain. We need a good implant surgeon."

Carmila looked a little alarmed. "You can't run Zeno jumps inside your brain."

"I can't resurrect either. This is strictly a onetime process. If anyone else goes in after the data and codes the way Gossamer did, everything will blow."

"And what will happen to you?"

Christine was extraordinarily calm. "My brain will be Cream of Wheat. I'll be a vegetable. It'd jam them up worse than a dead hand binder."

"It's a terrible risk," Marlowe said. "Suppose they go in anyway?"

"There'll be plenty of warnings. They won't risk destroying the codes. They'll deal. They'd have to be out of their minds not to."

"You'd gamble on corporate sanity?"

"I have to."

Marlowe rubbed his chin. He was starting to need a shave. "But if they do go in, you'll fall on your sword?"

"Is that sufficiently patrician for you?"

There was a long, long silence. In the end, it was Marlowe who broke it. "So where do we find this surgeon?"

Carmila got up and walked over to Christine's chair.

She stood behind it and stroked her hair. "Are you sure this is the only way?"

"Short of caving in and giving them what they want."

Marlowe laced his fingers and stretched his arms above his head. He suppressed a yawn. "Have you considered that as an alternative?"

Christine treated him to a withering look.

Marlowe shrugged. "I guess it was a stupid question. So what do you want to do now?"

Christine sighed. "The first thing we need to do is sleep. I figure we should hit the road again at sunset."

"To go where?"

"Somewhere anonymous. We're still on the run until the implant's in place. I need to make some calls. I can't take any chances with whoever does the implant operation."

"You'll call from here?"

"No, it's too public and too close to the city. I'll wait until we're deeper in."

Carmila had seated herself on the arm of Christine's chair. She slipped her arm around her shoulders.

Marlowe stood up. "Then I think I'll go and get some sleep."

Marlowe let the door close behind him, but he didn't immediately go to the adjoining cabin. The sun was coming up, blood-red against a hazy dawn sky. Marlowe took a deep breath. There was a slight smell of burning, but otherwise the air was clear. Perhaps their rooms were downwind from the chemical plant. He walked over to the edge of the dry pool. Its bottom was disintegrating as grass and weeds forced their way up through the faded blue cement. He reflected vaguely that the pool had to be a metaphor for a whole lot of things, but he was too tired to pursue the line of thought. Someone had dumped a pair of old tires in the pool. One had rolled to the deep end and lay at the bottom of a rusting chrome ladder. Much more recently someone else had carefully set a beer container on the edge. Marlowe walked over and kicked it into the pool. He wanted to be back in his apartment with his cat and his fantasies.

"You need a bottle of high test?"

Marlowe spun around in alarm. He'd thought that he

was alone. The woman who had spoken was short and dressed in a metallic green sweat suit that disguised her figure almost as totally as the huge black insect glasses hid her face. Her hair was tied up in a do-rag and she carried a red, white, and blue medium-sized Budweiser cooler.

"You scared the hell out of me."

"Your nerves are shot, man. Do you want a bottle or what?"

Marlowe had to agree with her. His nerves *were* shot. "How high's the test?"

"It's ten bucks high. I just sell the stuff, I don't make it."

She opened the cooler and pulled out a mason jar full of a colorless liquid. She unscrewed the jar and held it out to Marlowe. "You want to take a sniff?"

Marlowe brought his nose to the jar and inhaled. "Jesus Christ."

"You'd best mix it with a Coke or a Fling. I don't think it rates too good on taste."

Marlowe pulled out a ten. "I'll give it a shot."

He took the vendor's advice. He stuffed the bottle in his pocket and headed back to the restaurant to get some kind of soda to mitigate the predictable pain of the home brew. He had the feeling that he was starting to sink down the social scale.

The juke was still pumping although the restaurant was almost empty. The only people left were the truck jocks who had tried to harass Carmila earlier. They appeared to have been hitting the same high test that Marlowe had just bought, or at least something similar. Marlowe hoped he'd be able to get to and from the soda machine without being noticed. He was heading for the door with two cartons of Diet Cresta when they spotted him.

"So what happened to them two bitches? The threesome break up?"

Marlowe glanced back but kept on walking. "Don't ask me pal. I'm just the driver."

"Hey, wait up there."

One of the jocks was on his feet and lurching across the restaurant. There was no sign of the Holiday Court's security.

"Never one around when you want one," Marlowe muttered under his breath.

"Slow down there, pilgrim. I want to hear all about this."

He was a particularly unsavory specimen of his kind. He was squat and wide, built like a sumo wrestler, with a voice like Lee Marvin. The bulk could well have been the result of some pretty drastic chemical self-indoctrination in his youth. His leather jeans were stained and greasy, as was the black web harness that covered his otherwise naked and deeply tanned torso. In complete contrast, the stainless-steel toecaps of his heavyweight engineer boots were ground to a brilliant shine. Marlowe could imagine how efficiently they would crack ribs, a picture that was particularly easy to visualize when he looked at the man's small, angry slit eyes and the sneer under the drooping Zapata mustache.

"Are you telling me that two gash are shacked up together?"

Marlowe turned to face the truck jock. It was preferable to being stabbed in the back. He worked his face into a grin, as if he were going along with the joke. "I never tell tales out of school."

"What's the matter, boy? Didn't they give you a taste? Cut you out of the action, like?" He glanced back at his companions. "Seems like we got lesbian vampires here at the old truckstop."

The truck jocks all guffawed.

"I'd sure like to see that."

"Maybe loverboy here will introduce us."

The truck jock turned back to Marlowe only to find that he was no longer there. He blinked foolishly. "What the . . ."

Marlowe had taken the chance presented by the momentary distraction to slip through the exit. He hurried down the corridor at a half run. It might have looked cowardly, but there was no one around that he wanted to impress with his courage, and tangling with a bunch of moonshine-drunk truck jocks seemed to be a long way from the better part of valor. Marlowe ran around the pool and let himself into his cabin. He closed and bolted the door behind him, but he didn't turn on the lights. As he expected, within a minute or so, the truck jocks were lurching around the pool, yelling for him to come out. They kicked on a number of cabin doors, much to the consternation of the guests inside.

"Come out, you motherfucker! Come out right now!"

Their language was so archaic.

"We want those vampire dykes and we want 'em now."

Marlowe picked up the phone, ran his upper lip over his front teeth and did his best to sound like Humphrey Bogart. "Security? Listen, there's a gang of drunken jocks running amok out by the pool here. I think somebody should come and do something about them before they really get ugly."

Security was there in a couple of minutes. Confused shouting was followed by the thud of clubs and the crackle of stun guns. Then somebody pulled a firearm. The two reports and the two muzzle flashes in the night came almost simultaneously. After that, it was all over. There was a moment of stunned silence and then the truck jocks were herded away.

Marlowe turned on the light and sank down on the bed. "Is everyone in the world crazy?"

Without bothering to take off his trenchcoat, he pulled out the bottle of high test and uncapped it. He sipped it once.

"Christ." He was in pain. When he spoke out loud, his voice was hoarse. "It really does have to be mixed with something."

He set to drinking himself unconscious.

When he woke, the pounding in his head matched the pounding on the door.

"Marlowe, wake up! It's been dark for hours."

Marlowe groaned. He had no memory, and in that first moment of consciousness, he didn't want to have one ever again. Sadly, the amnesia didn't last. It all flooded back, every sadistic detail. He felt as though he'd been beaten up. The pain couldn't have been much worse if the truck jocks had actually stomped him.

"Marlowe, we've got to get going."

When he finally stumbled to the door, Christine and Carmila came in bearing coffee and donuts. There was the kind of sheen on them that indicated they'd spent the day making love. In the state that he was in, he found the idea close to repulsive. He looked at the donuts and swore that he'd never eat again. The coffee, on the other hand, was welcome. He held the cup in both hands like a child looking for reassurance.

"I feel terrible."

"Why did you have to drink so much?"

"What else was there to do?"

"We did okay."

Marlowe glanced up. Carmila looked smug and a little distant. Christine was much the same, although she didn't display it with the same defiant swagger as the vampire girl. Marlowe scowled. The hangover was reminding him that as well as the ever-present personal danger, there was no hope of any sexual gratification for him in the foreseeable future. High-tension hangovers were like that.

"I didn't have the same scope as you two. It's hard to have fun with only one." He went back to studying his coffee. The hangover was suggesting that he was being turned into the faithful eunuch. "I'd just appreciate it if you wouldn't flaunt it quite so violently."

"We don't flaunt."

"You both radiate it, right up to the tousled hair and dark satisfied circles under your eyes."

Carmila's expression moved to contempt. "Are you jealous of us, Marlowe? I didn't know you were a slave to the male drive. I'd imagined you were brighter than that."

"If I was bright, I wouldn't be here."

Christine was rapidly losing the afterglow. "But you are, so why don't you pull yourself together and let's get going."

Marlowe had very little to pull together. He hadn't even bothered to undress. The mason jar was on the night table. It was empty.

"I need a shower."

"You've got a half hour."

Forty minutes later, he found them waiting in the parking lot. Christine looked sour but didn't say anything. They walked to the gate of the security lot in silence. High clouds scudded across the night sky and sheet lightning played on the horizon. Somewhere, there was yet another storm brewing. For Marlowe, the silence was a merciful release. He didn't have the strength to sustain conversation. When he collected his gun from the guard on duty, the man stuck him up for a second gratuity.

"I already gave."

"Not to me you didn't."

"I feel like I'm being shaken down."

"You want this piece back or not?"

Just as the guard was pushing the Reaper through the slot in the armored Plexiglas of the security post, four hugh tractors wheeled through the main highway entrance to the lot. They were fun trucks, pulling no loads and wearing garish paint jobs. They rolled on hyped wheels and bubble tires and burned the totally illegal synthahol, spewing toxins like there was no tomorrow. The only place that such machines could operate was in the badlands, and Marlowe didn't care to think where the jocks who rode them acquired the ongoing fortune that must have been needed to run them. The lead truck was an old GA Goliath, pigged out in a full complement of crashbars, suicide fenders, and cow catchers, all in highly polished chrome. The cooling stack could have fit on the *Titanic*. The machine's bodywork was a bright canary yellow with a blood-red, geometric arrow curving over the cockpit shell. Behind it was a black Nissan Fatboy bearing a Satan motif. The front cockpit panel was a single bloodshot eye. A grimy but powerful hybrid followed while an antique Scammel, lovingly restored in white and gold, brought up the rear. Marlowe watched them as he broke the seal on his trenchcoat to replace the gun in its holster. The trucks pulled to a halt under one of the main floodlights. Cockpits flipped up and doors opened. The truck jocks and their riding pards swung down onto the tarmac like conquering heroes. Marlowe immediately recognized three of them from that morning.

"Damn it, we're in trouble."

Christine looked at the truckers. "What do you mean?"

"Those are the ones who were howling around the pool last night. They were after you and her."

Carmila didn't seem to immediately grasp the seriousness of the situation. "What did we do?"

"You were too damn weird for them."

"They're calling us weird?"

"Just get in the car."

To Marlowe's dismay, one of the truck jocks—the one with the sumo wrestler's body—was pointing in their direction. Marlowe unslung the Reaper. He glanced back at the security post. The guard was studiedly looking the other way.

"Come on! Move!" Marlowe snapped.

The truck jocks were advancing on them with the slow, confident amble of a wolf pack that thinks it has all the time in the world. Marlowe, Christine, and Carmila broke into a run. The truckers did the same. Christine was the first to reach the car. She fumbled with the locks. Marlowe turned to face the truckers. He held the Reaper at arm's length. There were shouts and guffaws.

"Loverboy's got himself a little gun."

Despite their amusement, the truckers were now advancing slowly and warily. One of them, an exceptionally tall individual wearing an ankle-length leather coat and a buzzwrap around his head, shook loose a set of freddy fingers. The thin, razor-sharp blades clicked and flashed as he flexed them.

Marlowe glanced back at Christine. "Will you hurry it up?"

"I've got it."

The door was open. Christine slid behind the wheel. The truckers were closing in on them. The one with the leather coat was grinning like a psycho.

"I don't figure he's got the balls to use that thing."

Marlowe could all too clearly imagine the five blades slicing into his flesh. He took a deep breath and fired a burst of 10mm above their heads. The truckers backed off. The Jensen's engine came to life.

"Marlowe, get in!"

He didn't need a second urging. He dived through the back door. Christine threw the car into reverse and Marlowe was pitched forward.

"Can you drive this thing?"

She didn't look back. "Of course I can drive this thing. I even took a defensive driving course."

The Jensen was screaming backward across the parking lot, laying smoke. Its headlights lanced through the darkness and spotlighted the trucker in the long coat. He made a lunge at the car. The freddy fingers scraped the paintwork. Christine had already electrified the outside of the car. There was a flash and a brief dimming of the dashboard lights. The trucker was thrown to one side. A couple of wild shots came after them, but both missed. The other truck jocks were dashing back to their tractors.

"They're going to come after us!"

"Let's get out of here."

The Jensen rocketed down the exit ramp and swung out onto the highway with a scream of tires. Christine desperately spun the wheel as they almost broadsided a slow-moving blue Ford pickup. As soon as she had avoided that disaster, she had to maneuver around the back end of a triple-rigged trailer. Finally, when there was an open road in front of them, Christine floored it. With one hand, she dialed up Wagner from the entertainment system. Marlowe wondered if it would do any good to close his eyes. The velometer hit 150K and went on rising. When it neared 200, the Jensen made a polite noise.

"This is an unsafe speed on the present road surface." As though emphasizing its point, the car bounced violently as it hit a pothole. "If you don't activate the override, I shall slow the car."

Carmila was peering through the rear windshield. "Here comes the yellow truck. It just turned onto the highway."

Christine hit the override.

"The yellow truck's gaining on us and the others are coming up behind."

"You seem unduly calm. Those maniacs are going to run us off the road if they catch us," Marlowe said.

"I love a car chase. It's all those old autohate movies."

Marlowe hung on to the seat in front of him. "Did autohate mean you hated yourself or you hated your car?"

"It's the same thing, isn't it?"

The Jensen leaped about a foot into the air. Marlowe hit his head on the roof. "We can't keep this up."

"They're still gaining on us."

"Without a load on, those rigs have got the speed, but they're still heavy enough to hold on to a road like this."

A light on the communication panel was flashing, indicating that there was nearby band activity.

"You want to hear this?" Christine asked.

"It's probably aimed at us."

Christine hit the CB toggle. Wagner's valkyries were immediately replaced by a nasal cowboy rasp.

". . . grease your ass. We ain't kidding. You hear us? You dykes are going to die . . . and the faggot with you!"

Christine cut it off. "These guys are archaic. They're like something out of the twentieth century."

"A lot of us are."

"Speak for yourself, Marlowe."

The road was strewn with debris, and Christine was forced to slow as the Jensen bounced and skidded.

"The yellow truck's coming up fast," Carmila reported.

The next stretch of road was relatively clear of garbage. Christine accelerated again. When the velometer touched 225K, the car issued a mandatory warning.

"To exceed the present speed while still retaining human control will result in the cancellation of all insurance coverage."

"That has to be the least of our worries."

Christine kept the gas pedal down hard. Marlowe turned around and craned out of the rear window. The trucks were uncomfortably close. They were like angry, speeding giants, festooned with dozens of red, white, and blue lights.

The radar was blipping.

"Damn," Christine said.

The headlights picked up a slew of cars across the highway. Christine jammed on the brakes. A carload of joads had hit a small truck coming off an access ramp; the accident had apparently started a chain reaction and a half-dozen vehicles were involved in the subsequent pileup. A beat-up red Fabian was lying on its side. A blue Nissan was a complete concertina, and something dead and bloody was hanging through the popped-out windshield. A gold Lotus was crushed flat under a truck. Scavengers were already moving among the wrecks.

"Going around this mess. Hold on to your hats," Christine warned them.

She spun the wheel and accelerated again. The Jensen mounted the hard shoulder at 100K bypassing the multi-car pileup. The headlights caught a dilapidated billboard reading "Let the Car Do the Driving." It had been erected by National Guidance Systems. They also had a fleeting glimpse of the joads whose car must have originally been loaded down with their belongings. They were brandishing crude weapons, standing off a gang of scavengers who had surrounded them like a pack of hyenas. Marlowe wondered if they were the same ones that he had seen in the restaurant. He doubted it. There were a great many homeless people traveling the roads.

The truckers reached the pileup and didn't bother to go around. They had the mass and momentum to go straight through. The yellow Goliath was still in the lead. It plowed into the wrecked cars like a ship cresting a heavy sea. It didn't even slacken speed. Smaller vehicles were thrown left and right. The other trucks did exactly the same as they came up behind. The gold and white Scammel pushed the red Fabian in front of it, creating a shower of sparks as the car scraped the road surface. The two machines smashed into the joads' car. A spark must have reached the gas tank of one of the wrecks. An orange explosion blossomed in the night. Dark figures and vehicles were silhouetted against the burst of fire. The joads and their attackers were totally engulfed. One figure, on the very periphery of the blast, ran back with flames streaming from its clothes. The Scammel went right on going, shedding pieces of blazing debris but seemingly unscathed. Somehow, though, the fire must have reached the Scammel's fuel. The synthahol blew and the tractor was consumed by a much larger explosion. Carmila bounced jubilantly in her seat.

"One down!"

"Yeah, but there's still three to go."

They were on a long, straight stretch of road with dead forest on either side of it. The three remaining trucks were running behind them, lined up abreast across three lanes.

"They're gaining on us again."

Christine eased off the gas.

Marlowe looked at her in alarm. "What the hell are you doing?"

"We're not going to be able to outrun them. If we keep this speed up much longer, we're going to run out of fuel."

"So what do we do?"

"I'm going to try something."

She continued to slow down. The trucks came closer.

"Someone's firing at us," Marlowe said.

There was the blinking flash of an automatic weapon from somewhere high up on the Goliath. Something spattered the outside of the Jensen. Marlowe and Carmila both ducked. Christine went right on driving. "Don't panic, the car's bulletproof."

The Goliath and the Fatboy moved ahead of the third truck. They were almost on top of the Jensen. They were positioning themselves at either side of the fugitive car.

"They're looking to crush us between them," Marlowe observed.

Christine actually smiled. "I was hoping they'd do that."

The two trucks were pulling alongside. Christine made no attempt to get away. Marlowe was horrified. "Are you out of your mind?"

A rattle of bullets hit the roof. Again Marlowe ducked. The trucks were running level. They started to swing outward. Christine was still grinning. "It's the sandwich play."

She spoke to the car. "Please arm the overdrive. I waive all the disclaimers."

"Overdrive armed."

"What are the disclaimers?" Marlowe asked.

"If you run the overdrive for more than ninety seconds the engine melts. It's a hijack gear."

She cut in the Wagner again. The music drowned all further conversation. The trucks were still level with the Jensen but a distance away. Christine slightly increased her speed. The trucks were coming back, closing fast and clearly intending to crush the Jensen between their armored sides. Christine did nothing. Marlowe was too scared even to close his eyes. There was something hypnotic about the huge yellow side of the truck relentlessly coming at him. He was able to count the bolts before Christine cut in the overdrive.

The Jensen seemed to leave the ground. The three of them were thrown back in their seats as Wagner was drowned out by the tortured, full-throat roar of the engine. Christine struggled to hang on to the wheel, unable to do anything but keep the car straight. They were out of the jaws of the crusher and rocketing down the highway. Marlowe prayed that they wouldn't hit anything. There was a crash from behind that sounded like the end of the world. The two trucks had hit each other and now seemed to be locked together. The big, evil-eye design on the front of the Fatboy appeared to have taken on a look of horror. They were staggering across the highway, drifting to the right. They hit the hard shoulder and kept on going. The Fatboy broke away from the Goliath and started to topple. It was rolling. The Goliath stayed on its wheels and went over the edge. It crashed into the dry dead trees and was lost from sight. The third truck, the hybrid, slowed to a stop. Inside the Jensen, there was an exultant howl.

"We made it!"

The car almost went off the road as Carmila hugged Christine.

"We made it!"

A ball of fire erupted from the trees. Something had happened to the Goliath. They pulled up. Christine cut the Wagner. Marlowe rolled down his window. The dead forest was starting to burn.

Christine started the car moving again. "I think I'm going to take the next exit and get off this highway."

"You want to take a blind exit in the badlands?" Marlowe asked.

"I don't think we should be on this road at any cost."

Marlowe shrugged. "Suit yourself."

SIX

THE CHATEAU ECSTASY WAS ALMOST MAGNIFICENT. IF nothing else, there was the sheer scale of its tawdriness. It seemed to take up half of the hillside with its tarnished but still flashing come-hither that was the electronic equivalent of a heavy-lidded, hot-pink pout.

"You've driven us to a goddamn love palace."

Carmila gaped like a delighted child. "I couldn't imagine a better place to hole up! I thought that these extravaganzas had been torn down years ago."

Christine laughed and shook her head. "I swear I didn't know it was here. I just took the exit at random. It must be the very last of its kind."

The Chateau Ecstasy and all the other establishments like it had been built at the peak of the great binge of sexual euphoria that had followed the discovery of the ID3 vaccine. They had been sprawling Disneylands of erotic variety with space and equipment for both the amateur and the professional. The Chateau Ecstasy was far from being either the largest or most magnificent of its kind. Compared to the big ones in California and Nevada, it was a back-road attraction. Its real claim to fame was that it had survived. The others had been bulldozed under as soon as ID3 had mutated into the viable ID4 and the party had come to a grinding halt. It was an irony that the Chateau Ecstasy had been saved by having been built in what would later be declared badland. Its hillside was worthless real estate and there was no reason to tear it down. It had become the dinosaur playground of the nostalgic and the strange. Obviously it had suffered the ravages of time and the badlands. The skysigns had become virtually indecipherable, and the tall, squirming holograms had turned green and magenta and were losing their integrity. By day, the buildings looked sad and weather-beaten. Besides the ordinary peeling paint and bad patch jobs, large chunks of the sugar and gingerbread frosting on the central tower had fallen away, leaving exposed areas of vinyl sheet and sprayrock. By night, however, it still had the magic of a sleazy Shangri-la.

The offers of fun started well before the Jensen reached the main gates to the love palace. Like the Holiday Court, it had developed a crowded and extensive shantytown outside its walls. Prostitutes of every kind lined the approach road, each one doing his or her best to attract the attention of those passing by on their way to the main gates. The Jensen had to run the full gauntlet of their ideas of what might be alluring. There were exposed breasts, bared thighs, peekaboo buttocks, and costumes that either left nothing to the imagination or else demanded too much. Lace and leather, plastic and rubber all did their best to kindle a spark that might cause the occupants of a car to pause on their way into the love palace proper. Some prowled on their own, while others gathered in groups, standing around garbage fires that took the chill off the night air. Jugs of home brew were being passed around, and there was a surface festivity to the crowd. While some were content to strike a hip-tilted pose and wait to get lucky, the more aggressive hustlers jostled right up to the car and rapped on the windows. A blond transsexual in full KDJ uniform, complete right down to the gold eagles on the shoulders, pressed his/her face close to the glass next to Marlowe and mouthed a supposedly imperious order.

"You will come with me right now."

"The hell I will."

As in the Zone, there were a lot of masks, but in the faces that were exposed, there was an underlying desperation.

"This is kind of depressing."

A young man decked out for action in corset, fishnets, a feather boa, and far too much mascara positioned himself directly in front of the car and refused to move. Christine snarled as she braked. "Get out of the way, you mincing idiot."

The young man refused to step aside until she actually nudged him with the front fender. As they passed, he treated them to a string of obscenities. Marlowe shook his head. Leisure-outs tended to forget just how privileged they really were.

"Maybe it'll be better inside," Christine said.

"I sure as hell hope so."

Christine seemed to be taking it all in her stride. "Whatever it's like, it's an ideal place to hide out. There must be a dozen ways to conceal your identity."

"How long do you plan to stay here?"

"As long as it takes to arrange for the implant."

"You're definitely going to go through with that?"

"I don't see that I have any other choice."

The main gate was straddled by a huge, fanciful, pink neon sculpture of a heterosexual couple energetically copulating in a gravity-defying position. Behind the facade, however, the net and razor wire that extended in either direction and protected the perimeter from unwanted intruders was absolutely functional. Like the Holiday Court, the Chateau Ecstasy had its own armed security force, although these wore simple sweatsuits with the palace's logo on the back instead of Student Prince uniforms. Once again, the Jensen on its own was quite enough to get them instantly admitted.

When they'd been through the parking and check-in process, Christine went directly to the nearest pay phone and made three brief calls after indicating clearly that she wanted Marlowe and Carmila to remain out of earshot. Marlowe could only be impressed by the ease with which she roused what he could only imagine to be highly placed and trusted corporate underlings from their beds. She came back looking grimly satisfied.

"The arrangements will be in place by morning. I'll call again at dawn."

Suddenly, the three of them were at something of a

strange loose end. They'd been running for so long that having nothing to do was perplexing.

"I guess we could take in the attractions," Christine suggested.

The Chateau Ecstasy was a mixture of ten-year-old high tech and derelict. They had entered what amounted to the central midway of a sexual theme park. Holograms, neon signs, light boxes, and fiber-optic wavers beckoned from every direction. Right beside them, a flurry of lasers in a carbon-dioxide cascade pitched the steamy anonymity of the Orgydrome. Carmila nudged Marlowe. "You want to check it out?"

Marlowe shrugged. "Sure, why not."

They bought tickets and entered what proved to be a low-ceilinged dome. Inside, a circular tier of bleachers ringed a central arena that was kept filled with drifting steam from outlet pipes positioned at regular intervals around its outside. Some two dozen naked people squirmed and frolicked in the mist while roving spots of colored light played across their sweating bodies. The whole exercise was accompanied by a numbingly loud pressure dub.

"If someone from the fifteenth century walked in here, they'd think that they were in hell."

Marlowe, Christine, and Carmila settled themselves in the bleachers. Marlowe bought a beer from a hostess who was naked except for the vending tray that was attached to her by an intricate arrangement of vinyl straps. He watched her walk away. The hostess's exaggeratedly high heels did interesting things to the way she walked, and the crisscross black vinyl that circled her body had an air of antique bondage porno. He sipped his beer and turned his attention to the moving mass in the pit. His eye was caught by the somewhat bizarre coupling of a voluptuous blonde and a very energetic dwarf.

Carmila glanced at Christine. "You want to go down there?"

Christine shook her head. "It's a little too public for me."

"That's not what you said the last time."

"That was different. I knew some of those people."

Marlowe couldn't stop himself from looking curiously

at the two women. What did they really do when they were alone?

"Are you going to join the dance, Marlowe?" Carmila asked.

"Much too public for me."

After a while, the curling thrust of mass squirm and wallow began to tire. Carmila was the first to start motivating for a move, and no one was at all reluctant to return to the midway. They passed by a number of routine touchfeel booths, and although Carmila hesitated in front of the House of Pain, they kept on going. Marlowe was more than content to stroll aimlessly. It was a relief in itself not to feel hunted. The people around them were quite as interesting as the attractions. In many respects, the theme park was not unlike the Zone. All those people were there exhibiting their fantasies. The major-league sexual stereotypes were all on parade, from the meek to the macho. A dominant walked a brace of submissives as though they were Irish wolfhounds. A line of cheerleaders did all they could to attract customers, as did a team of muscle boys in tatoos and chains. Geishas were inscrutable behind their traditional, doll-mask makeup, and, in a strange way, so were the twentieth-century disco sluts, hiding in hot pants, lip gloss, and electric eyelashes. The love park was, above all, a place to meet strangers, to make love to images and facades. It was a magic kingdom where the ineffectual could wield imaginary power and the powerful could purchase degradation. The nervous could delight in a not-quite-controlled scent of danger. Inside the booths and arenas and the secluded and darkened rooms, a naked body could be a suit of armor, if one had its language right. Marlowe supposed that the scene could have saddened him if he'd been in a more reflective mood, but right then he was content simply to be distracted. He was in enough trouble on his own account without worrying about a bunch of sex crazies.

Christine was the first to stop being a tourist and join the party. She had spotted a young male bodybuilder with a shaved head, a heavily oiled torso, and a set of truly magnificent muscles. She walked directly to where he was posturing alone, seemingly in a world of his own, laid a small white hand on his bicep, and stood on tiptoe to whisper something in his ear. Carmila, who had been left behind with Marlowe, let out a low hiss. Her face was set for controlled hostility. Christine came back to where they were standing, dragging the bodybuilder behind her.

"I think I'm going to spend some time with Mr. Universe here."

Carmila scowled. "Do I come, too?" Christine shook her head.

"I was thinking about a one-on-one situation. We'll rendezvous at dawn in front of the Orgydrome."

Even Marlowe was surprised at the casualness of the dismissal. Carmila waited until Christine was out of earshot before she snarled.

"Bitch!" She looked to Marlowe for confirmation. "Did you see that? The way she just dumped me? After I saved her ass for her."

"The megarich can be highly capricious."

"They can rot."

"They tend to assume that everyone is a potential lackey."

"I'm no lackey."

Marlowe had no intention of becoming the straight man for a tirade. "Explain that to her."

Carmila bared her teeth at him. Suddenly she was all vampire again. He almost expected her to pull out one of her concealed weapons and use it on him. "You don't know anything, Marlowe."

"You can't expect fidelity from someone like Christine Stavers."

"It's not a matter of fidelity. We matched blood, damn it."

Marlowe had no idea what matching blood might entail, but he had a quick gothic vision of some depraved and messy candlelit ritual in a black vampire hole that culminated in a glimpse of a transfixed Christine with blood running down her chin. He quickly abandoned the fantasy before he had to guess from whom or what the blood had come.

"I don't care about some muscle-bound goon. She can screw who she likes. She just should have taken me with her. She knows that we're tied until this thing is over. Damn her! Damn her!"

Carmila's outburst was starting to attract attention. A middle-aged, would-be victim in powder-blue relaxurs and a lot of gold chain was staring at her with doglike adoration. He was plainly imagining her spikes gouging his cringing flesh. He started to move toward her with a crablike diffidence. His mouth was working as though he was trying to find words. Carmila only spotted him at the last minute, but her rage was instant. She kicked out at him with a pointed boot. "Get away from me, you slime!"

The would-be victim let out a whimper of unwholesome pleasure. Carmila kicked him twice more. Marlowe couldn't resist being the voice of sanity. "He seems to be enjoying it. Getting his kicks, so to speak."

Carmila lost all control. She whipped out a length of chain and seemed about to start beating the man with it. Marlowe moved to restrain her, but in the same moment she collected herself. "You can't win with these crawling bastards."

"Why don't we walk for a while? Maybe we'll find something to take your mind off Christine."

Carmila regarded Marlowe with undisguised contempt. Her voice was acid. "You don't take your mind off a breaking of blood ties."

Marlowe decided that there was no worse pain in the ass than a vampire scorned. "Pardon my ignorance."

They walked on through the freak show in silence. Carmila continued to fume. Marlowe made one last try to divert her anger.

"Aren't you taking all this a little seriously?"

"Don't you take your life seriously?"

"Up until three days ago, I didn't have a care in the world. I was happily living in my private Humphrey Bogart movie."

"So how do you like reality?"

Marlowe scanned the menu of freaks that were cruising the midway before he answered. A Cat Woman in scarlet latex was giving him the eye. "I'd have to take that under advisement."

They went on walking past a tall, cylindrical tower of

translucent glass that claimed to be a free-fall simulator. Carmila was concentrating so hard on her fury that she took only scant notice of the midway attractions. The only mercy was that she was now quiet. Marlowe looked back for the Cat Woman, but she had already moved on. He was beginning to become a little resentful. Despite its decay and sleaze, there were a lot of interesting possibilities in a place like the Chateau Ecstasy. Christine expected to meet them at dawn, but Marlowe didn't see why he had to nursemaid a petulant vampire through the intervening four or five hours. Surely he had as much right as anyone to a little illicit fun. God only knew when he'd get another chance.

He tentatively broached the subject. "Do you have any idea of what you want to do for the rest of the night?"

"I don't give a damn. I'm too angry."

"Suppose we just make the best of what we have here?"

"Screw you, Marlowe."

Suddenly a knot of what looked like urban vampires, completely out of their element but in full somber splendor, came down the midway toward Carmila and him. At the sight of Carmila, they stopped in their tracks. Marlowe was immediately poised for flight. Without a weapon, running seemed to be the best policy.

"Are these some of Yorga's bunch?"

Carmila shook her head. "I've never seen them before." Her sullenness seemed to have completely evaporated. "I think I'll go talk to them. I want to know if they're for real or if they're just weekend bloodsuckers."

"They look pretty real to me."

Carmila shrugged. "They do to me, too, and if they are, they're my kind of people."

The vampires were simply standing and staring. There were seven of them, four men and three women. Their black capes flapped gently in the night breeze. One of the men was unnaturally tall and emaciated. His face was made even more gaunt by the heavy application of luminous makeup that glowed pale green even over the lights of the midway. Carmila started to walk slowly toward them. Marlowe made a move to stop her. "Wait."

"Get off my ass, Marlowe. Don't make this any more complicated than it needs to be."

Marlowe showed both palms in a hands-off gesture. "Whatever you say."

As Carmila approached the group, the vampires' body language changed noticeably, reminding Marlowe of what happened when a lone wolf made overtures to a strange pack. He'd seen it once on a nature show. The shift was most marked among the three women. Where initially they had only been watchful and supercilious, Carmila's proximity brought out a hissing hostility. One of them undulated an arm in a gesture as graceful as that of a Balinese dancer, except that instead of a fan, she briefly unfurled a three-bladed lotus razor. The gesture was clearly a challenge, but Carmila pointedly ignored it. The men weren't showing any hostility at all, even seemed marginally pleased to see her. At the very least, she might be a temporary mate for the odd man out. Carmila halted a couple of paces from the group. Marlowe was too far away to hear what they were saying, but her attitude seemed almost submissive. The four males surrounded her. The women stood their ground scowling. The tall one in the luminuous face paint asked a number of questions to which Carmila gave lengthy answers. From their hand gestures, it appeared to Marlowe that some of the questions referred to him. After the bloodshed in the parking lot of his apartment building, he didn't altogether relish the idea of being the subject of a vampire's conversation. Finally Carmila started back to where Marlowe was standing.

"I'm going off to spend some time with these people."

Marlowe nodded. "Suits me."

"I thought it probably would."

Marlowe tilted his head in the direction of the vampires, who were watching the two of them intently. "What did they want to know about me?"

"They were wondering why I was hanging around with a forties creep."

"And what did you tell them?"

"I said that you were nervous about being out in the badlands and you'd hired me as your bodyguard."

"Cute."

"Does that hurt your pride?"

"It doesn't do much for it."

"They bought it, and that's what really counts."

Marlowe tugged at his earlobe. "Are you going to be there to meet Christine at dawn?"

"I don't know."

"What's that supposed to mean?"

"Exactly what it says. I don't know. I don't know how I feel about La Stavers. Maybe she can go and get her brain messed with on her own. She clearly doesn't need me."

"So I'll either see you or I won't."

"Don't look as if it bothers you, Marlowe. You don't even like me."

With that parting shot, she turned on her heel and went back to the other vampires. They moved off up the midway. Carmila was walking ahead with the men. The women brought up the rear, scowling and clearly unhappy about the new arrival. One of them threw Marlowe a look fit to kill. Marlowe was profoundly glad that he hadn't chosen to be a vampire. It must have been a hell of a thing keeping up all that hate.

It took a couple of minutes for Marlowe to realize that he was truly on his own. The thought that Carmila might no longer be a part of the trio occupied the front of Marlowe's mind. If she was going to bail out on Christine, why should *he* stick around? What was to stop him just taking a powder and vanishing? The temptation was strong, but the answer was all too painfully simple. He didn't have any options. At a very minimum, one corporation wanted to do the extreme prejudice on his ass, and Yorga's tribe almost certainly desired much the same, only their way would be much slower and more painful. He had enough scrip of his own to last barely a week and if he used his credit, anyone could nail him. Shit, he didn't even have the codes to the Jensen. All he could do was to stick with Christine and hope that if she saved her own skin, she might save his along with it.

"I am in one hell of a vise," he said aloud.

"Isn't talking to yourself a sign of something?"

"He looks like a man who's forgotten how to whistle."

"You remember how to whistle, don't you? You just put your lips together and blow."

Marlowe could scarcely believe that they were standing there laughing at him. "Are you a hallucination?"

"Not us."

"We're real real."

Marlowe shook his head, still not believing what he was seeing. The first impression was one of perfection. The two of them were right out of one of his wildest wet dreams. Just one woman who looked like Ida Lupino in *High Sierra* would have been enough of a surprise, but two, and within an ace of being identical, strained the bounds of probability. Their suits, with the wide shoulders, tight, knee-length skirts, and wide, deep lapels that revealed a considerable amount of cleavage, were tailored from vertically striped satin. The pillbox hats with little veils were made from the same material. The ensembles were completed by white shoulder bags and black-and-white wing tip high heels. The pair's most striking feature was their perfectly matched red hair. This wasn't the ginger that was usually referred to as red. This was a bright fire-truck red, and Marlowe had never seen anything like it even in the Zone. The overall effect was of a strange Andrews Sisters singing group with one member missing. They were a forties dream.

"I'm Velda."

"I'm Velma."

"Where did you two spring from?"

"We've been trailing you for some time."

"We thought you looked like one of us."

The word *trailing* had given Marlowe a moment of anxiety, but he could hardly imagine that anyone would go to all the trouble of sending these two after him. No one would put on a costume show when an ice pick in the back of the neck would be more than adequate. Marlowe was hardly important enough to merit that kind of treatment.

"What's your name?" one of them asked.

"Marlowe." If this was some ludicrously elaborate setup, a phony name wouldn't save him.

"So what were you doing with those two weirds?"

"The two women?"

"They didn't look like your style."

"They weren't. They'd hired me as a bodyguard." Marlowe took a certain pleasure in turning the gag around.

Velda and Velma seemed to be waiting for Marlowe to make some kind of move, but when he failed to come up with one, they weren't shy about coming to the point themselves.

"We thought you might suggest that the three of us go somewhere."

"You're a little slow, Marlowe."

"I'm sorry. Put it down to my being under some recent stress. I'd love to go somewhere with the two of you, but I'm not sure where to suggest. I only just got here."

"Oh, we've been here for three days. We know all sorts of places."

Marlowe grinned. "I guess the first thing I need is a drink."

"For the stress, right?"

"Right."

They started walking. Velda was on one of his arms and Velma on the other. Marlowe had one moment of nagging doubt. If these two were professionals, he might be in for a certain amount of embarrassment.

"Uh . . . listen, girls. I've got to tell you that I'm not really overburdened with money."

The two came to an abrupt halt. "Does that mean we have to buy all the booze?"

Marlowe quickly shook his head. "Hell, no, I can take care of that kind of thing. All I meant was . . ."

"All he meant was that, if we're a couple of whores, he can't afford us."

"We're not whores, Marlowe. Okay?"

"We're just enthusiasts. Okay?"

They started walking again. Their first stop was a little beyond the midway at a small bar that, to Marlowe's relief, sold real branded booze. While Velda and Velma chattered, Marlowe looked at himself in the mirror behind the bar. It was the first time he'd had a chance to take stock of himself in what seemed like months. He needed a shave and there were dark circles under his eyes, but he didn't look too bad. In fact, as far as he could tell, he was actually closer to resembling the hard-bitten private jingle of his fantasy than he had ever been. His black, slicked-back hair was a little too long to be strictly accurate, but that was the way things went in a fantasy. He was glad that, unlike some, he never had succumbed to the idea of having the full Humphrey Bogart face job. There was nothing wrong with his face as it was. His nose was straight, his jaw was square, and if his blue eyes weren't quite as cold and relentless as they ought to be, they would probably get that way before this whole Stavers caper was over. The only real drawback was his mouth. It simply wasn't tough enough. The lips were too full and too ready to smile. It didn't worry him too much, though. A sufficient number of women had told him that they liked his lips that way.

Velma caught him looking at himself. "Like what you see?"

"Sorry, I was thinking about something else."

"You're not supposed to be thinking of anything but us."

"We have to be the finest offer that you've had in a long time."

Marlowe, who was drinking straight scotch, quickly downed his shot. He chased it with a little beer. "Believe me, I appreciate that fact."

"So why were you looking in the mirror?"

"Like I said, I was thinking about something."

"The stress again?"

"That's right."

Velma glanced at Velda. "You don't think we've got a narcissist on our hands, do you?"

"I sure as hell hope not."

"Maybe he's just trying to convince us that he's got a mysterious secret."

"Do you have a mysterious secret, Marlowe?"

"If I did, would I tell you?"

"He has a point there."

"He's from the Zone, okay? They're all like that."

Marlowe twitched. He hadn't told them that he was from the Zone. "Does it show that much?"

"Of course it does. You people are unique."

Marlowe wasn't absolutely convinced, but he also didn't resist when Velma took hold of his arm.

"Why don't we get him out of here and away from the mirror, and see if he'll give us his full attention."

They led him out of the bar. They appeared to be heading away from the midway and into a darker and more free-form section of the love park. Marlowe wasn't quite able to get his bearings because Velma and Velda kept up a constant chatter. They exhibited a radical need to explain to him how they had come to be at the Chateau Ecstasy.

"We drove up here from Alphaville, okay? It was, like, getting so down time, back there. Dreary cybernauts putting the crowd on everything decent in the locale, you know?"

"Nothing but silver clothes."

"All the forties were either changing lanes or else leaving town or, worse still, they were getting into this weird Charles Parker beret thing and hanging out with Keithkids and, you won't believe it, for Chrissakes, actually shooting heroin. God knows where they got it from, but that was the way things were going in Alphaville. Everyone else was getting blocked on diazins, and the naziboys were marching around the streets with banners and flaming torches, just as bold as you like."

"And if it wasn't them, it was the Blood of the Lamb, parading around and screaming and hollering, statiking the hookers and burning all the paper they could four five one. It wasn't a fitting place for the likes of us. I mean, we could have been in Airstrip One."

"Airstrip One?"

"Of course, you wouldn't have heard about that yet. That place is just too too oblique. Hip?"

Marlowe looked a little bemused. Velda had lapsed into deep Alphagirl. Alphagirls, irrespective of the fantasy they followed, were strange about their dialect. They kept constantly mutating their speech patterns to the point that almost no one who wasn't an Alphagirl could be exactly certain what they were saying. Lacking any more intelligent comment, he just nodded and looked interested. "I guess so."

"Anyway, we finally had enough and we packed everything into the short and started back this way."

"It was like we were in some joad fantasy, not our style at all, but enough is enough. We were way past our threshold."

"We probably would have given the badlands the go round the roses. I kid you not. Who needs the depression, not to mention the radiation, except that Velma had heard that this was the last of these places and we decided to take a look at it. Velda saw a show about it on TV, didn't you, Velda?"

"I read about it in a magazine."

"Velda reads magazines."

Velma seemed extremely proud of her companion's accomplishment. Marlowe acknowledged that. "There aren't too many who do that anymore."

"Do you read magazines, Marlowe?"

"Not too many magazines, but I do have a collection of antique comic books. The Spirit, Captain Midnight, Watchman, Swampthing—all that stuff."

He felt a momentary pang for his cat and his apartment and his stuff—all those parts of his missing life. Velma was looking up at him.

"That's very impressive."

Marlowe wasn't sure if she meant it or if she was putting him on. They had passed through a Roman garden with fallen columns and erotic statues of fake marble, and they were entering a grove of plastic palm trees. Don Ho music was being pumped from concealed speakers. Ragged holograms of hula dancers swayed in the darkness, lifesize plastic flamingoes stood among the trees, and a number of naked and half-naked couples were making love on the Astroturf, apparently unconcerned about who might be watching them.

"You know what we should do? We should take Marlowe to a cube. Then we'd have him all to ourselves."

The cubes were private love units built according to the most minimal of designs: perfect cubes, maybe twelve by twelve by twelve meters, made in one piece from form-poured silate. They came in a variety of bright, primary colors and stood like giant featureless dice in a neat row between more plastic palms. They had no windows and just a single door. Signs above the doors indicated that all but two were vacant. The cubes were a little way up the hill from the plastic coconut grove, and Marlowe and the women had to make their way up a steep, winding path. The path was lined with benches that were also occupied by lovers who seemed to have no particular need for privacy. The climb took five minutes and Marlowe arrived at the row of cubes a little out of breath. He told himself that he had to quit cigarettes.

"Which color do you fancy, Marlowe?"

"The white one would go with your outfits."

"You haven't seen our lingerie yet."

"How about the red then?"

"How did you guess?"

The cubes were fully automated, activated by the insertion of a credit cone into the reader beside the door. Marlowe reflected that the gentlemanly thing to do would obviously be to proffer his credit—but if he used it, everyone in the world would be able to locate him. And if he didn't use it, whatever excuse he came up with, if Velda and Velma were anything other than a simple pair of Alphagirl funsters, they would immediately suspect that he had something to hide. The sensible thing would have been to cut and run, and yet he hesitated. He dearly wanted to go into the cube with these nearly identical women. When he finally came up with an excuse, it sounded nothing short of lame.

"I hate to tell you this, but I have a slight problem with my credit."

Velma placed her hands on her hips and Velda raised an eyebrow. Marlowe plunged on.

"I've got a whole bunch of scrip, and if one of you would run this on your cone, I'd happily make it good."

"You really push it, Marlowe."

"Are you on the run or something?"

"Something."

Velda and Velma held a quick conference for Marlowe's benefit.

"Maybe he's just too much."

"You think we should dump him?"

"He doesn't make much effort to create a good impression."

"Maybe he takes his hard-boiled image very seriously."

"Maybe he takes it too seriously."

"You really want to eighty-six him?"

Marlowe came to his own defense. "Maybe I could say something."

"What?" The word came like a chorus. Two pairs of less-than-friendly eyes turned in his direction.

"Well . . . I don't like to put it this way, but if I had picked you up, I wouldn't have placed myself in this situation. I'd have made damn sure that I could pay the freight. As it is, you came up to me and, unfortunately, I'm in something of a jam at the moment."

"Are you telling us that it's our fault?"

"The very nerve."

Marlowe quickly shook his head. "Listen, sweethearts, I don't mean that at all. What I'm saying is that it's just a matter of damn bad timing. You can walk away from me if you want to, but it'd be one hell of a shame. We forties ought to stick together."

Velma was the first to soften. "He does have a cute line."

Velda wasn't quite so easy. "He probably uses it all the time."

Velma was fumbling in her shoulder bag. She finally produced a credit cone. "What the hell, it's only money."

She inserted the cone into the reader. There was a very brief delay and the door to the red cube slid back. The interior was bare and functional, totally without the titillating frills that Marlowe might have expected. Bare conduits angled across the ceiling and down the walls, and the basic support frame was fully exposed.

"It's kind of brutal, isn't it?" he commented.

The cube's austerity was almost military, not unlike a much bigger version of the slot coffins that provided the most minimum overnight shelter back in the Zone. Marlowe had spent more than one night in their cramped confinement when he was too drunk to make it back to his apartment. He noticed that the two women were grinning at him.

"You've never used one of these before?"

Marlowe blinked. "I never did and I think I know why."

The worst thing was the light. It was white, relentless, and capable of destroying any passion.

"Don't worry, Marlowe. This is only the getout light, okay? We haven't turned the place on yet."

Velma reached under the huge bed and produced an old-fashioned bulb remote. She manipulated it, and the room suddenly exploded. There was a flash of blinding light and then everything went pitch-black save for a swarm of angry red electronic blips chasing each other around the room at a dizzying speed. His head whirling, Marlowe was forced to sit down on the bed. That had gone to pneumo.

Velma cursed. "Everything in this place is screwed up. The damn thing's running from climax out. It's ass backwards."

"Everything in this place is coming apart. Why don't you image me up on the end wall?" Velda said.

Marlowe realized that he had misjudged the cube. The night might be even more fun than he had imagined. He was actually inside a box of electronic effects and goodies, something like a room-sized version of a Sony Wholeworld. It was a three-dimensional illusion center. Velda had put her bag on the bed and was standing facing the wall farthest from it. Velma manipulated the remote. A hugh image of Velda appeared on the wall. The blips vanished and everything else was dark velvet. The bed stabilized to a firm, warm gel.

Velda critically examined her magnified image. She seemed fairly satisfied with what she saw. "None too shabby."

She began to unfasten her jacket. Marlowe took off his fedora and watched transfixed as she slid the garment down over her shoulders. She was stripping in the old classic manner. A gentle, dark blue moire pattern was moving across the ceiling. Velma had moved up beside Marlowe and was easing him out of his trenchcoat. She nodded toward Velda and breathed in his ear. "Isn't she terrific? And I don't have to be jealous, because I'm just like her."

Velda's suit was gone. Velma was bringing up the audio, sweet swelling strings with a slow, insistent subpulse. Velda stood in her underwear, swaying gently to the music. The big image mirrored each movement. Marlowe realized that he was watching what had to be the start of a whole choreographed show.

"You two are really something."

"We're the best, Marlowe."

Velda's lingerie was a wicked scarlet; if the garments weren't custom made, they were lovingly preserved, antique Fredericks. The peekaboo brassiere with its insets of see-through lace, the high-waisted panties, and the self-supporting stockings were like something out of an old Betty Page comic. Marlowe couldn't help but smile. Velda had even left the pillbox hat perched on the top of her head. It was all so perfect, as if they'd had him dreamscanned. He was having such a good time that the thought passed without the slightest shadow. His coat and jacket were off, and Velma was working on his shirt. She paused for a moment and then pressed something into his hand.

"Take these."

Marlowe could feel the shape of three capsules, but it was too dark to see any color or markings. "What are these?"

"What's the matter with you, Marlowe?"

She'd hit him in the reckless pride. He dry swallowed the caps and wondered what would happen. Velma and Velda changed places. Now Velda was beside him on the bed and Velma was taking her clothes off. She stood with her back to the screen, her image towering behind her. Marlowe and Velda kissed as she unfastened his pants. He raised his hips as she slipped them off. Velma's underwear turned out to be black.

"It's so you can tell us apart, Marlowe."

Velma removed her bra. Velda, without letting go of Marlowe, reached out for the remote. The scan narrowed to a tight closeup of Velma's breasts. Marlowe was starting to hallucinate. There were faint rainbows at the edges of the giant breasts.

"Why don't you turn on the shatterpix?"

Velda once again manipulated the remote. The ceiling and all of the walls were filled with composite images.

They were huge and pink and wetly gynecological. Velma joined Marlowe and Velda on the bed which was now pulsing softly. They were both kissing him. Neither had removed their shoes or their hats. The images shifted quickly, dissolving one through the next in no logical pattern except that they were someone's idea of what might be erotic. Marlowe had a fleeting glimpse of a dark-haired woman attempting to copulate with a donkey. The brief clip was in grainy black and white, Havana in the 1930s. The donkey looked profoundly disturbed. Marlowe was aware that only one woman was touching him. He turned his head. Velma was digging into her bag. She came out with a pocketmed.

"You don't mind, do you? A girl can't be too careful."

Marlowe shook his head. He hated medchecks and always feared the potential bad news, but he hardly felt that he was in a position to refuse. Velma pressed the pocketmed against his thigh. The leds glowed green and amber.

"You're a healthy boy."

"I do my best."

An arm holding a sword broke the surface of a mirror-smooth lake while a vast caressing female hand, wearing an emerald ring, moved over the ceiling. It was a detail of the young pretty blonde who was busily arousing herself on the left-hand wall. The music had dropped to a sonorous rumble, heavy with subsonic massage, against a trilling counterpoint of whale song. It seemed to Marlowe, who was now quite naked, that hands and lips were touching every part of his body. His right leg quivered involuntarily. A breast rubbed against his arm. He could no longer tell to whom any individual part belonged and he didn't particularly care. He was being carried along on a warm, viscous tide of sensuality and he didn't want to know where the hell he was going. The bed was in liquid response and it amplified every movement. The hand on the ceiling was replaced by a whip-wielding stripper in a black leather corset and net stockings. She had the washed-out hues of aged Technicolor. The scan closed on a small section of the woman's stockings, moving closer and closer until the ceiling was an abstract pattern of net and flesh. Two young black men with oiled bodies wrestled on the far wall. Pumas mated left and right. The bed seemed to be growing warmer.

"Okay, Marlowe?"

Marlowe just groaned. A train plunged into a tunnel and huge breakers crashed on a deserted beach.

"Why can't this damn stuff sync in? What's all the pow zoom?"

The sequence of images turned grim. It started with sadoporn and went straight on to the just plain nasty. Twentieth-century bondage loops and docudomination rapidly degenerated to the home movies of a creatively depraved secret police officer. Three men in military uniforms were forcing a screaming young woman into a faceless metal helmet that would cover her whole head. There were a number of colored cables attached to it. The shaky, hand-held video picture was unpleasantly real. There was an inexplicable flash of James Dean masturbating.

"Get this thing off, okay?"

"Doesn't this goddamn cube have mood sense?"

"I'm telling you, Velma, kill the shatterpix."

"I can't find the damn bulb."

Marlowe realized that it was under his knee.

"Cut to abstract, right now!"

Marlowe fingered the bulb. A bright, colored image of the three of them was splashed over the ceiling and the walls. It wasn't the real-time image. It must have been recorded some minutes earlier. Marlowe was fascinated.

"An instant replay."

Marlowe had seen himself recorded in the act before, but never projected so large.

"That's not abstract, Marlowe. That's reality."

"How did we get ourselves in that position?"

"Abstract, Marlowe. Okay?"

Marlowe reluctantly manipulated the bulb a second time. They were back with the red blips and the black velvet. This time, however, the blips weren't chasing each other. They were dancing in unison formation to a slow waltz.

"That's better."

It didn't take them long to regain their concentration, and Marlowe entered one of the most exhausting nights of his life. One thing that had never been included in his twin fantasies was the way that they could spell each other. One might be resting, but he could be sure that the other was ready to go. They took him in relays until it was almost dawn, with only brief intervals when he staggered to the vending unit for another beer. It was only by accident that he discovered the time. A chance remark cause Velda to search in her bag for her watch.

"It's six eighteen."

Marlowe sat up in bed and groaned. "It must be nearly dawn."

"So?"

"So I have to get myself out of here."

Velda and Velma looked at him in bleary surprise.

"Why, for godsakes?"

"I have to meet some people."

"The two weird women?"

"Yeah."

"You're crazy, Marlowe."

Marlowe flopped back on the bed. "Probably."

"What do you want to go and meet them for when you could stay here with us?"

Right at that moment, all he wanted to do was curl up and go to sleep. He was starting to feel dizzy.

"You could drive back to the Zone with us."

"Yeah, come with us, Marlowe."

Marlowe shook his head. "It's a nice idea, sweethearts, but there are some people in the Zone who want to kill me."

"Is this some deep fantasy game or what, Marlowe?"

Marlowe slowly sat up again. "No, it's no game."

He swung his legs over the side of the bed. His head and his kidneys protested. He stood up and the protests became more intense. He started to gather up his clothes. Velda was hastily pulling on her panties.

"Hold up, Marlowe, we'll come with you."

"You don't have to. It's been a monumental night, but I'm afraid that it has to end here."

"We know that."

"We don't want to marry you, okay?"

"There isn't any reason that we shouldn't walk you to

whatever, is there?'' The two of them were now almost dressed.

Marlowe shrugged into his trenchcoat and put on his fedora. ''I can't think of one.''

Velda and Velma smiled. ''Then that's settled.''

They left the cube arm in arm. Once again, Marlowe had a woman on either side of him. He was rather glad of them. The fresh air had done nothing to ease the pain and, without them, he might have staggered. The dawn was a deceitful pink that even invested the tawdry towers of the Chateau Ecstasy with a certain daybreak innocence. It was an innocence, however, that didn't extend to the midway. Down its length, a half-dozen figures were sprawled unconscious amid the garbage that littered the rubberized walk. An old GE cleaner robot was slowly working its way through the mess, sucking up the debris into its drumlike interior. Each time it came across one of the sleepers, it skirted around him or her, leaving each in his or her own individual island of candy wrappers and beer containers. At the far end of the midway, a bunch of greez was unsteadily James Deaning its way toward the main gate. The sun had just tipped the horizon and those first rays were reflected from their chrome facemasks. Marlowe looked for Christine outside the Orgydrome, but there was no sign of either her or Carmila. At least she wouldn't be ragging him for being late.

''Isn't that one of your weirds?''

Christine had appeared around the corner at the end of the midway.

''That's her. I've got to go.''

Velda presented her face. ''So kiss me good-bye, okay?''

''Kiss us both good-bye.''

Marlowe leaned forward and Christine screamed. She was struggling in the grip of a black-cowled figure. Marlowe's jaw dropped, all thought of kissing instantly erased.

''Gatsu?''

Marlowe couldn't believe that he was actually seeing a Gatsu. They only belonged in movies, not in this hazy midway dawn. Two more Gatsu came out from the alley beside the free-fall tower. Another two appeared from behind one of the touchfeel booths. They closed on the kicking and hollering Christine, moving with their trademark lope. The greez had turned and were watching with interest. Marlowe took in the scene with a great deal more alarm.

"I'm dead."

There was no way that he could take Christine away from five trained Gatsu. Any one of them could break him into chicken parts with their bare hands. They wouldn't even have to resort to their considerable arsenal of concealed weapons. He looked around for a possible route of flight.

"Stay right where you are, Marlowe."

All trace of Velda's Alphagirl voice had vanished. She was hard, cold business. Velma's hand was in her bag.

Marlowe stood stock-still. "I should have known you were something else."

"Oh, we're something else, all right."

Velma's hand was out of her bag. It was filled with a 20/20 Remington minimag finished in white metalflake. "Place your hands on your head."

"Are you going to kill me?"

"We never kill anyone."

Marlowe looked to where the Gatsu had finally subdued Christine. "Them?"

"Right."

"We hand you over to the Gatsu. That was our instruction."

"So what was the rest of the night about?"

"We had to keep you out of circulation until the Gatsu had taken possession of Stavers."

"But how did you know I was coming to meet her?"

"You really aren't very good at this, are you, Marlowe? You've been pinned since you left the Zone."

They walked toward the five Gatsu and Christine. Marlowe only had one hope left. The Gatsu had gone to considerable trouble to take Christine alive. Maybe they'd do the same for him. He wished that he could come up with something better.

The bloodcurdling scream took everyone by surprise. Two Gatsu held Christine; the other two spun around ready for anything, falling into the familiar combat crouch.

Velda and Velma both stiffened. Velda also had a gun out, a white 20/20 identical to her companion's. Carmila and her band of vampires came down the midway at a dead run, howling like banshees, making straight for the Gatsu. Knives flashed in the morning sun. The vampires seemed to have increased in number since Marlowe had last seen them. There were now at least a dozen of them. Marlowe didn't want to imagine how Carmila had convinced them that they should rescue Christine. Maybe it was just the promise of wild and gratuitous violence. Whatever their motivation, they seemed completely unimpressed with the Gatsu reputation for invincibility. The Gatsu stood their ground. More knives had appeared from the wide sleeves of their costumes. Vampires and Gatsu met in a flurry of windmilling arms and a chorus of grunts and curses.

The vampires fought with a ragged, open-style fury that was a total contrast to the Gatsu control, and yet they were able to hold their own. Admittedly the Gatsu were outnumbered more than two to one, but Marlowe had still expected a near-instant massacre. A Gatsu and the tall vampire went one on one in a sinuous, acrobatic tango that would have been beautiful except that each man held a pair of razor-sharp rainbow knives. There was a scream. One of the vampires had gone down. Marlowe thought that this first blood might be the end of it, but the vampires fought on. The Gatsu were so hard-pressed that the two holding Christine had to let go of her and defend themselves. Christine broke out of the melee and started running up the midway to where Marlowe was standing with the two women. One of the Gatsu hurled a vampire off his back and dropped to one knee. He had a steel blowpipe in his hand. He put it to his lips and fired a dart at the fleeing woman. A moment later, the Gatsu was down. The vampire that he had thrown off had recovered and brought a folding mace down on the back of his cowled head. At first, it looked as though the Gatsu had missed Christine. She took two more steps—but then she faltered. Her legs seemed to give out under her and she went sprawling on the walkway. Marlowe sighed.

"I guess that's the end of it. Nobody's going to get her secrets now."

"She's not dead, Marlowe. The Gatsu are better trained than that. She'll wake up with nothing worse than a headache."

While Velda covered Marlowe, Velma hurried to where Christine was lying. Even though Christine was out of it, the fight still went on. The vampires fought as though they were insane, but they were being forced to give ground. Marlowe knew that in a matter of minutes they would have to break and run, or be cut down on the spot. Three of them were down already and there was blood spreading across the midway. As Marlowe watched, a fourth staggered backward clutching his throat. A Gatsu had slashed through his jugular with a butterfly knife. Blood was spurting between his fingers. As he fell, it became horribly clear that his head had been all but severed from his body. Marlowe's moment of truth had only been delayed for a brief respite.

The burst of machine-gun fire produced an instant reaction. Everyone froze. Even the tall vampire and the Gatsu fighting with him paused in the middle of their drawn-out encounter. A large squad of men was coming down the midway from the direction of the main gate. The majority were Chateau Ecstasy security, but they were keeping themselves well to the rear. The front line was made up of some twenty or so young men in neat, formal dark suits carrying automatic weapons. At the head of the whole group, the apparent leader was holding a bullhorn. He raised it to his mouth.

"Everyone please remain absolutely still or I shall order my men to open fire."

The vampires and the Gatsu carefully disengaged and disentangled, moving away from each other to form two separate groups. The dead and wounded lay between them. The young men in suits moved forward with their weapons at the ready.

"Who the hell are these guys?" Marlowe asked.

Velda scowled. "As far as you're concerned, it's the cavalry to the rescue."

"It is?"

"These are Stavers's people."

"Thank god for that."

"You can say that. Now we're in trouble."

The line of neat dark suits halted abruptly. A Gatsu staggered and fell. A second one did the same. The remaining two fell together.

Velda shook her head. "Toxin D caps. Same old hollow teeth. That's the trouble with Gatsu. They still suicide out when a gig goes sour."

Marlowe raised an eyebrow. "And you don't?"

"Hell, no. We survive."

The neat dark suits had reached the vampires. Carmila, who hadn't actually taken part in the fighting, seemed to have a lot to say to the one with the bullhorn. She pointed to the unconscious Christine a number of times and twice to Marlowe. Almost immediately, he, Velda, and Velma were surrounded by polished, impersonal young men pointing machine pistols at them. The leader with the bullhorn seemed completely unruffled by what had just transpired. Not a single blond hair was out of place, and his pink boyish face was so scrubbed and smooth that Marlowe could almost believe that he hadn't even started to shave. The only features that gave the lie to this seeming innocence were his pale blue eyes: hard, cold, and quite deadly.

"So you're Marlowe."

"I'm Marlowe. Who are you?"

"I may well be your savior, Marlowe. I may also be the only one at Stavers Industries that Christine can trust."

"You have a name?"

"I'm Dancer."

"I'm glad to meet you."

"Hmm."

Dancer didn't seem to have a very high opinion of Marlowe. Behind him, some of his men were inspecting the bodies of the Gatsu. Others were watching the vampires suspiciously. Marlowe felt it was time to intercede on their behalf. It was also an opportunity to score his first point off Dancer.

"You ought to tell your Boy Scouts to lighten up on the vams. If it wasn't for them, Christine would be long gone. They bought us the time it took for you to get here.''

''I'll decide what to do with those freaks.''

''Suit yourself. I just thought I should fill you in on who our friends are.''

''And you, Marlowe, are you a friend?''

''I don't have any choice. I'm in for the duration.''

''With friends like you, Marlowe, perhaps Ms. Stavers has no need of enemies.''

''I don't like you, Dancer.''

''Should that concern me?'' With that, Dancer turned his attention to Velda and Velma. ''I ought to shoot you two on the spot.''

''But you know you can't, don't you, Dancer?''

Velda and Velma actually seemed to be enjoying the situation.

''We're accredited operatives with class-one licenses.''

''Shoot us, Dancer, and it's a murder rap for you.''

Dancer glanced at Marlowe. ''Did they kill anyone?''

Marlowe shook his head. ''No.''

''Did they do you any harm?''

Marlowe smiled. ''Quite the reverse.''

Dancer looked increasingly bleak. ''I didn't think you two would be working for RAMco. I thought that Smith and Jones had more class. Didn't you boast back in San Cristobal how you'd never had to take the corporate big-buck?''

''You don't know that we are.''

''Sure you are.''

''There are more players in this game than you suspect, Dancer. Look at Marlowe, here. He's further into the game than you are and he doesn't have half a grasp of what's happening. But you know something? He'll still be in it when they've buried you.''

Dancer looked at Marlowe with contempt. ''You think so? This piece of fantasy tail? He was almost Gatsu meat. You were going to give him to them.''

Velma had the bland expression of a woman winning a point. ''But he's still here, isn't he?''

Velda drove it home. ''You know why Marlowe will always have the edge on you, Dancer? It's because he doesn't have a fetish about rules. He doesn't care if he's here or Humphrey Bogart."

"Who gives a damn what we said in San Cristobal," Velma added.

"You're just too clean, Dancer."

Dancer lost a little of his executive sangfroid. "I could hold you for questioning, maybe lose you in the system for a month or more."

"You won't do that either. You know the trouble we can cause."

Dancer all but snarled. "Get out of here."

Velda and Velma both laughed. They quickly hugged Marlowe. Velda whispered into his ear, dropping back into her Alphagirl accent. "Take care of yourself, okay? Nobody else will."

Marlowe watched them walk away with open admiration. A world in which Velda and Velma existed had to be doomed. Smith and Jones? He wondered what they would be next. Elsewhere, the attention was now focused on the still unconscious Christine. The prevailing opinion seemed to be that she'd be out for hours. Carmila was calling to him.

"Come on, Marlowe. We're getting out of here."

Marlowe swayed back into reality. They were moving out again. He shook his head trying to make some sorry sense of the way the nonstop chain of events was crowding him. His life was turning into some roller-coaster ride. This had to be what armies were like and he was some poor bloody conscript.

"Where are we going?" he asked.

Medics in white one-piece uniforms had appeared with a stretcher and were loading Christine onto it. Marlowe was walking in step with Carmila. The neat suits were executing a fast but orderly withdrawal. The vampires had already melted away. The curious crowd that had started to gather gave everyone involved a wide berth. The head of Chateau Ecstasy security started complaining to Dancer about the bodies. Dancer used the minimum number of words to let him know that it was his problem.

"The suits came in two gunships and a jump jet,"

Carmila informed him. "They're out beyond the perimeter. You, me, and Christine are going in the jump jet."

Marlowe sighed. His experience of flying was very limited, but it had been enough to convince him that he didn't like it. "With Dancer?"

Carmila nodded. "With Dancer."

"So where are we going in this jump jet?"

"The Sheila McKenna Clinic."

"That's where Christine gets the implant?"

"Right."

Carmila didn't look entirely happy about it.

The aircraft were parked close together on a flat patch of brown, disease-ravaged grass beyond the shanties that ringed the pleasure park. The two Rhino gunships squatted, hump-backed and sinister, with their rotor blades dipped and their weapons systems bristling. They were finished in dark gray, night-operation camouflage that was only broken by a red Stavers Industries logo on their upswept tail fins. The Morgan jumper was a complete contrast. It was gleaming white with gold trim, and although the logo on its tail was also red, it was less aggressively the color of blood than the ones on the choppers. More neat young men in dark suits formed a ring around the planes, presumably to protect them from the vagrants and nonpeople. It scarcely seemed necessary. The Rhinos, which were the exact same model used by Population Management, had the hobos thoroughly intimidated. They stood off at a good safe distance, staring with sullen unease at these arrivals from the sky.

"Hurry up, please. There may be other RAMco operatives on their way."

Marlowe was very aware that he was being routed again. First Velma and Velda, and now these suits. It was starting to get to him. He was sick of being run around like a rat in a maze. He was tempted to lash out at the young man who had spoken but he restrained himself. If he did, he knew that they would just immobilize him and toss him on the plane anyway. He contented himself with snapping at a young man who attempted to help him up the steps of the jump jet. "I'm not a cripple, goddamn it."

They settled into their seats and strapped in. The still

unconscious Christine was maneuvered inside and placed in a seat. The engine noise rose to a high-pitched whine. With a slight shudder, the plane started to rise. Outside there was the louder scream of the Rhinos and the percussive slap of their rotors. After maybe a minute or so, the nose of the jump jet suddenly dipped. Marlowe couldn't keep himself from grabbing for the seat arms. The Morgan was now in forward flight.

SEVEN

DESPITE HIMSELF, MARLOWE DOZED. HE'D HAD SO little sleep in the last few days that his eyes sank shut before he could do anything to resist. When he woke, the plane was cruising over an orderly patchwork of green fields. He glanced at the nearest neat young man who was sitting across the aisle cradling his machine pistol in his lap and being careful not to get gun oil on the pants of his immaculate suit.

"We're out of the badlands?" Marlowe asked.

The neat young man shook his head. "Not yet, but the western border defenses, the Parker Line, should be coming up anytime."

"It's kind of green down there."

"They maintain a wide sanitary cordon on this side. The farm states take disease control very seriously."

Shortly the pilot's voice came over the intercom to confirm the young man's prediction. "Those of you who might be interested, if you look out the right-hand windows, you'll see the Parker Line in all its majesty."

Marlowe craned and looked. He'd seen the Parker Line countless times on TV, but nothing had prepared him for the awesome scale of the thing. It was a dark, rolling slash cross the landscape, a wide, straight river of steel and concrete, razor wire, and brown plowed earth.

Blockhouses and guard towers stood like islands in the stream.

"Damn thing could stop an army."

"That's what it was built for. If it wasn't there, the vags from the eastern seaboard would swarm over the last good land like locusts."

That was the standard line of the conservative normal. Before Marlowe could reply that the Parker Line was also a monumental piece of applied fascism, the pilot came back on the intercom.

"I'm afraid we're going to experience a slight delay, folks. I've just received a message from Population Management. There's a PM action being staged directly in our flight path and we're going to have to maintain a holding position until they get through. There's nothing we can do about it. The PM have priority over everything in this airspace. The only consolation is that we'll have a grandstand view of them doing their thing while we're hovering."

From the air, the crowd was indeed like a swarm, thousands of tiny particles massing at a single point on the line, pressing forward as though they believed that they could defeat steel and concrete by sheer weight of numbers. They appeared to have broken through the outer line of wire and were attempting to scale the first steel wall. As far as Marlowe could see, the assault was doomed to be stopped there. Beyond the wall was a strip of dragon's teeth. If there weren't actual troops in among the pointed cement blocks, there had to be fixed fire remotes. Anyone who made it over the wall would be cut to pieces.

"They've got to be crazy."

Marlowe was starting to really dislike the neat young man across the aisle. "They've got to be desperate."

"Who knows what happens to vags when they start massing."

"You sound like they were a different species."

"Aren't they?"

That effectively put an end to the conversation.

"Gunships coming in."

Four PM Rhinos were coming fast and low out of the badlands. They were a garish black and yellow. The PMs believed in high visibility. The sun was now well up, and the choppers' shadows raced across the grass in front of the jump jet. The mob pressing up against the defenses began to lose some of its solidity as those on the outside started to flee. All at once the ships opened fire. The rockets left lance-straight trails in front of and behind the helicopters as they streaked straight into the crowd. They burst in billows of greenish-yellow gas. The gunships lifted slightly as they crossed the line and executed a graceful formation turn before coming back for a second pass. The crowd was rapidly being dispersed, running in apparent panic, in any direction that was away from the fence and the relentless helicopters. When they were spread out over the open ground, the gunships broke formation and started harrying the attackers individually. With amazing speed, what had once been an angry and cohesive mob was being scattered into smaller and smaller groups.

"It'll be a long time before that bunch starts m[illegible] again."

Marlowe didn't say anything. Then the pilot put an effective cap on the incident.

"We have permission to resume forward flight. We're sorry about the delay, but these things are quite beyond our control."

The Sheila McKenna Clinic was set in its own secluded estate in the middle of low rolling hills. There was even live woodland where a stream wound its way down one of the shallow valleys. As the jump jet made its approach turn, Marlowe was treated to a full aerial view of the place. Low, black glass buildings were arranged around the central courtyard shaped like an irregular hexagon. A tall silver obelisk stood at the center of the courtyard. Even from the air, it was plain to see that the clinic had been designed to give the impression of cool, institutional perfection. There was a mathematical precision in the use of open space that clearly indicated that no expense had been spared. It nestled in the fold of the hill with a certainty and confidence that seemed a million miles away from the crowding in the Zone or the desperation of the badlands. This was top-of-the-line health care at what had to be top-of-the-line prices. The superrich really did live in a separate world.

"That's some spread," Marlowe commented.

"That's not even half of it. The majority of the complex is underground. They hollowed out most of the hill. It's a sealed environment that uses a lot of the same technology as the moon bases."

Marlowe continued to stare at the place as the plane started to slow. There was something decidedly chilling about a moon base on Earth. A landing pad was positioned at a distance from the main complex. The plane slowed and started to drop toward it. There was nothing more than a slight sway as it settled down on its vertical jets and came to rest on its landing legs. The neat young men put on their sunglasses. Supervised by Dancer, they picked up the still inert Christine and moved her to the door. A motorized gurney, accompanied by four orderlies in medical sealsuits, was waiting at the edge of the pad. The gurney rolled forward. When Christine was safely loaded aboard, it started up the dignified gravel drive that led to the buildings. Dancer climbed back into the cabin where Marlowe and Carmila were still sitting in their seats.

"You two are something of a problem. Ms. Stavers gave no specific instructions as to what should be done with you."

Carmila met his gaze. "We're her companions."

"I realize that. What I don't know about is the nature of that . . . ah . . . companionship."

"Aren't you taking rather a lot on yourself?" Marlowe asked drily.

"I'm taking on the safety of my employer, Marlowe, and when it comes to that I intend to take no chances regarding who or what you are."

Carmila made it clear that she considered him an underling. "I don't see what the problem is. If what you've told us is true, Christine will be awake soon enough and you can ask her."

"Unfortunately not."

"What?" Carmila was instantly a picture of feral suspicion. "What's going to happen to her?"

"After she's detoxed from the dart, she'll be resedated

and prepared for the implant surgery. Her orders were that it must be done as quickly as possible."

"So what does happen to us?"

"You'll be admitted as no-therapy patients. You'll be treated with courtesy, and every effort will be made to see that you're comfortable. You will not, however, be permitted to leave the facility."

"So we're prisoners."

"That's correct."

For a moment, Marlowe thought Carmila was going to pull something. Then her common sense prevailed. She unbuckled her seat belt and stood up. "We intend to wait for Christine, in any case. You may as well show us where we're supposed to stay."

Dancer nodded. "I'm glad you're willing to cooperate."

Carmila looked at him with contempt. "What did you think we were going to do? Jump you and hijack the plane?"

"I'm paid a lot of money to expect the unexpected."

As they walked up the gravel drive, Marlowe had a chance to look at the Sheila McKenna Clinic from ground level. It was much larger than it had seemed from the air. There was something almost monastic about its geometric serenity. The towering obelisk and the angular glass gave it the look of a temple to high science.

At the surface level, the complex was all but deserted. Apart from birds singing in the trees that ran along one side of the drive, the place was practically silent. Three gardeners in khakis and sun helmets manicured the already perfect grass that ran downhill from the main structure all the way to the landing pad. Their shears made a soft snicking sound. When they reached the hexagonal courtyard, which Marlowe could now see was, in fact, a wide expanse of white marble, two elderly women in white medical kimonos took an agonizingly slow stroll, watched from a distance by a pair of orderlies in what appeared to be the standard sealsuit.

Marlowe, Carmila, and Dancer crossed the courtyard in the direction of a pair of wide glass doors. At their approach, the doors slid open with a soft sigh. It was dim inside. The lights glowed with a strange violet tinge and the air was chill, with an oddly metallic, almost electric edge to it. This reception area was dominated by a huge portrait of the accident-prone first lady after whom the facility had been named and where, as one of its first patients, she had been virtually reconstructed. The painting had been done by Mozrite, at the peak of his bleak period, in somber blacks and browns. Aside from the picture, there was nothing in the area except for a single, polished-steel reception desk and moving clusters of surveillance cameras. Two clinic security men in white cop uniforms stood by, along with a young, redheaded doctor who looked sleek and capable in rollcollar and mini. Marlowe noticed that she had exceedingly good legs. She seemed to be waiting for them.

"Are these the ones who are going no-therapy and restricted access?" she asked Dancer.

"That's right."

"I should take them from here."

Dancer stiffened. "I understood that I would control the security in this matter."

The doctor firmly shook her head. "That is definitely not the case, Mr. Dancer. You are Dancer, aren't you?"

"I'm Dancer."

"Well, Mr. Dancer, it was clearly explained to your people that we have our own, very efficient security, and that if you and your security personnel were allowed into the facility at all, your role would be strictly to backup and monitor."

"That's not satisfactory—" He read from the nametag on her tunic. "—Dr. Kenwood."

The insult was noted. She folded her arms across her chest. "It's going to have to be. If you can't accept our terms, the clinic is reluctantly going to have to discharge the patient."

Marlowe was starting to enjoy the power struggle. He tried to direct a half smile of support to the doctor, but she ignored him. At least Dancer was bright enough to realize that he was all the way onto someone else's turf. He backed off.

Dr. Kenwood turned her attention to Marlowe and Carmila. "Are you aware of the details of a limited-access, no-therapy admission?"

''We know we're prisoners.''

Dr. Kenwood was brisk. ''That's nonsense. There's no such thing as a prisoner in a hospital. You commit yourself on a conditional admission, and we simply carry out your instructions. In your case it would be room restriction.''

Carmila pointed at Dancer. ''That's not our instruction. That's his.''

Kenwood looked coldly at Dancer. ''Is this another problem?'' She looked as though she had no patience with those who caused problems.

Marlowe shook his head. ''No, there'll be no problem. We know that we're in for as long as she is.''

''Then we'll need to have you validate the insurance coverage.''

But this time Marlowe wasn't going to give ground. ''We don't validate anything.''

Dancer was quick to jump in. ''They don't have identities in this context.''

Kenwood looked as though she wasn't at all happy about that. ''Then they'll be registered as absolute risks and you'll be billed accordingly.''

Dancer made an impatient gesture. ''Of course. The cost is of no importance.''

Kenwood faced Marlowe and Carmila. ''If you'll please follow me.''

She led them through a wide, empty corridor to a bank of three elevators, talking as she went.

''Because of the conditions of your admittance, you will be housed in the minimal contamination area on the fourth sublevel. Before you can be admitted to the area, you will have to go through a full decontam.''

They rode down in the elevator. Marlowe wondered how a facility like this could be so deserted. There was something spooky about the muted lights and emptiness of the starkly functional interior. He saw no other people and could only assume that they were being deliberately isolated.

The decontamination unit was the first place Marlowe had seen so far that actually resembled a hospital. Amid bright lights, polished-steel walls, gleaming equipment, and flickering monitor screens, technicians were waiting.

They went straight to work with a smooth, impersonal efficiency, separating Carmila and Marlowe by screens and gently but firmly removing their clothes. Marlowe found himself standing on a low pedestal. A tubular Plexiglas cover was lowered over him and needle jets of warm water hosed him down from all sides. The water shut off and the tube was filled with pink, sweetly chemical vapor. He stood there for almost a minute wondering if he ought to breathe, then a rush of air blew in from under his feet and the vapor was gone. The cover rose. Marlowe was about to step off the pedestal but the technician stopped him.

"Please remain where you are and put these on."

He handed Marlowe a pair of dark protective goggles. Marlowe did as he was told. When the cover lowered again, he was subjected to twenty seconds of intense violet light. Finally he was released.

"Okay, you can step down. You're clean."

The technician held out a white kimono and a pair of cotton slippers. Marlowe put them on.

"What happens now?"

"I'll take you down to your room."

Kenwood had reappeared.

"My clothes—what will happen to them? I was kind of attached to that suit."

"They will be cleaned and stored until you're discharged."

"And where's Carmila?"

"She's already been processed through."

"Will I be able to talk to her?"

"There will be no communication until the restrictions are lifted."

"Complete isolation?"

"It's the most practical way."

"I always like to be practical."

"Since you have no identity here, you will be referred to as Adult Male K30."

"Cute name."

For the very first time, Dr. Kenwood permitted herself a faint smile. "We thought you'd like it."

They went through a double containment lock and down in another elevator. The corridor that led away from the elevator had the same black walls and muted violet lights as all the others, and was lined with numbered doors.

"I've been meaning to ask, what's with the Castle Dracula decor?"

"The what?"

"The general gloom. Doesn't it depress the hell out of the patients?"

"We don't encourage the patients to wander the corridors."

"But why's it like this at all?"

"Background sterilization. We can't afford to have anything getting in from the outside."

"The air around here looked pretty good."

"It may look good and it may even smell good, but in medical terms, all outside air, no matter how fresh, is still a soup of bacteria and toxins. It just isn't acceptable in a modern health facility. This isn't the twentieth century, you know."

She stopped in front of door 30. "This is your room."

"Adult Male K30?"

"Think of yourself as a unit."

"I'd rather not. I'm still trying to hold on to my humanity."

Dr. Kenwood ignored the remark. "You'll find a full menu of services on the bedside terminal."

She pressed a pen-shaped instigator against a pad beside the door. The door slid open.

"Please step inside."

Marlowe hesitated. He was aware that Kenwood was watching him intently, clearly on her guard should he balk at going into the room or otherwise cause trouble. He made a small gesture of surrender and stepped through the door. It closed behind him and he was on his own. He looked slowly around.

"Jesus, Marlowe, how in the hell did you get to be Adult Male K30?"

The room was spartan and relentlessly white. The whole damn place seemed to be black and white. Did they have something against color? There were no windows, but a fifty-cm wallscreen was positioned as though it was supposed to be some kind of minimal substitute. The only light came from a pair of recessed panels and a small reading light on the bedside table. A frosted-glass door led to a tiny toilet and shower. The center piece of the cell—Marlowe had already started to think of room 30 as a cell—was the adjustable contour bed. As well as the reading lamp, a small desktop terminal was positioned on the bedside table, exactly as Dr. Kenwood had predicted.

Marlowe sat down on the bed. A small surveillance camera was mounted high up near the ceiling so it could scan the whole room; he assumed there were other sensors built into the bed. He sat for some minutes, doing nothing but listening to his own breathing. Confined in such a place, he would have to watch out for his sanity, first and foremost. The isolation alone would be bad enough, but he knew that locked in here, totally under the control of faceless observers, he'd be a sitting duck for anything they might want to do to him. He had no idea of their intentions, but it was all too clear that if they so chose, his brain was laid out for washing.

Sitting around and working up a head of paranoia was hardly the best way to start this stretch of isolation. He decided that he should explore the possibilities of the room. How bad could it be? The normal occupants of room 30 were the ailing rich. He reached for the terminal. Noting that it was a simple tone touch, he wondered why it wasn't voice-command activated. He ran his fingers over the keypad, and the wallscreen flickered into life. He opted for the "Introduction" and "General Menu." The introduction was a routine welcome to the clinic and a lengthy assurance that no finer or more advanced medical care existed anywhere else on the planet. The tone was overly reassuring and heavy with bedside manner. He moved on to the general menu. As far as books and movies were concerned, there were more than enough to keep him occupied even if he were shut in room 30 for a year. The interactive software would probably keep him going for another two with its wide variety of games, puzzles, math problems, and tactical exercises. He could play chess with a master and refight every battle from Waterloo to Yemen. Even his physical welfare seemed to be covered by a selection of exercise regimens and workout tapes that went all the way to an exercise in psuedo 3D that was supposed to prevent confinement-induced myopia. All this was in addition to ninety channels of broadcast TV. He wanted to protest that he couldn't spend the time until they decided to let him out staring at a screen, but a deep streak of brutal honesty reminded him that, back in the Zone, he had spent an awful lot of his time doing exactly that. The Sheila McKenna Clinic didn't appear to stint on its patients' entertainment or comfort. As well as a schedule of regular meals from a menu that exceeded the scope of any luxury hotel, there was a selection of snacks and tidbits that should have satisfied the most demanding glutton or gourmet. The only prohibition seemed to be against drugs, alcohol, and tobacco. Marlowe was not sure he could withstand that deprivation. He wondered who would bring his food and fill his room-service requests—maybe they'd be bribable. Somehow he doubted it. They would most likely be more examples of the humorless efficiency that he had already encountered. Even if there was some space for loose behavior on the part of the orderlies, it would undoubtedly be squashed by the omnipresent camera. In any case, the point was academic. Even if he found a chink of corruption, he had nothing with which to bribe.

He decided that he might as well test the system. Now that the excitement was over, he was ravenously hungry. He scrolled up the snack menu and touched a turkey sandwich and a glass of milk. A wash of abstract color appeared on the screen while his order was digested. After a few seconds, it was replaced by a computer-simulated head and shoulders.

"Your order is being processed and will be delivered to you momentarily. Please do not hesitate to make any comfort request."

The bland neutrality and indeterminate sex of the simulation fitted perfectly with the whole sterile atmosphere of the clinic, and Marlowe took an instant dislike to it. The milk and sandwich arrived in about five minutes, as far as Marlowe could tell. Looking around, he realized that nowhere in the room or on the extensive data menu was any means of telling time. He didn't like that. It was one more detail that fed his brainwashing fears.

The orderly who brought his food was almost as bland as the simulation. The smile as he set down the tray meant absolutely nothing. "How are we this afternoon?"

"I'm fine. I don't know about you."

The door closed and Marlowe was alone again. He stretched out on the bed and dialed up a movie. Within the first ten minutes of *Portrait of a Mobster*, he was fast asleep.

Nobody seemed to want to do anything to his mind. The worst problems were boredom and the lack of cigarettes. He watched movies and old TV shows, and his day was punctuated only by the arrival of meals. He ordered an unnecessarily large number of items from room service, simply because it gave him something to do. He discovered that there seemed to be three orderlies assigned to him. Two were little better than robots. They arrived. They set down the tray or made up the bed. They smiled without making eye contact. They asked, "How are we today?" He would make some stupid and vaguely hostile remark, and they would leave. The third one was a gay male who tended to linger longer and chatter. The chatter said absolutely nothing and was strangely innocuous. It seemed to Marlowe as if the clinic, as well as being physically sterile, had programmed all color out of human behavior. Then Marlowe realized that there were a number of things that had been programmed out of his own behavior. He was no longer frightened; he couldn't even raise a healthy anxiety. He knew that this incarceration was, at the very best, a brief respite in the continuing drama that was racking up an alarming total of fatalities and giving him no reason to believe that it would be any different in the immediate future. He should have been paralyzed with fear, but he wasn't. Even the expected nicotine withdrawal was hardly noticeable. He assumed that his faceless observers must be raiding him with something. The fact that the clinic made such a fetish of a clean environment suggested that they were unlikely to be filling the air with micpsychs, although there could well be tranks in the food. The most logical answer wasn't chemical at all. The wallscreen was all too probably pumping him full of an alpha overload. Once again,though, the point was academic. He wasn't about to stop eating or turn off the screen, so all he could do was to lie back and enjoy it.

On the third day—calculating a day as three meals and a period of sleep—he was idly scrolling through the entertainment menu when he came across a section that he had previously overlooked: "Personal Services." He attempted to open the file, but the screen would only flash the words "seek clarification."

"So clarify, goddamn it."

The screen talking head appeared. "Sensitive to the sexual needs of its patients, The Sheila McKenna Clinic offers physician-approved gratification for most preferences unless orders specify otherwise. There are no such restrictions in your case, Adult Male K30."

"No kidding."

'If you require the service, please touch accordingly."

Marlowe didn't hesitate. A lengthy and very specific questionnaire appeared on the screen. Marlowe began checking the answers.

It was some time before she arrived and when she did, there was something strange and clinical about the whole encounter. She was fashionably pretty; a slightly too pointed chin and eyes that were rather too small and narrow were about the only two things that would have kept her out of the cosmetic commercials. She was versatile, skilled, and energetic. The strangeness came with the absolute lack of even simulated passion. Her hands and mouth were cool and precise, and even the convulsive jerks of her pelvis were quite detached. Marlowe had, however, chosen exactly the right costume. The old-fashioned nurse's uniform was perfectly starched, although perhaps a little too short to be strictly accurate. The white stockings were held up by a lacy garter belt and the matching shoes had extremely high heels. She stayed for exactly an hour, and after she'd gone, Marlowe could scarcely believe that the episode had happened. Perhaps they were trying to drive him crazy after all. And the worst part was that he really didn't give a damn anymore.

On the fourth day, by the same method of reckoning, the routine was abruptly interrupted. Marlowe was lying on his bed watching Audie Murphy in *Bullet for a Bad-*

man and feeling increasingly like a vegetable when the talking head interrupted the movie.

"Adult Male K30, Dr. Kenwood will be with you in five minutes."

Marlowe had been wondering when something was going to happen. If they had taken Christine directly into surgery, surely she must have regained consciousness by now. He might have been worried if he hadn't been so doped out. Whatever they were using on him seemed to have a cumulative effect. When the door slid open and Dr. Kenwood stepped inside, Marlowe could only stare stupidly.

"I have some news for you," she announced.

"What have you been using on me? My brain has turned to creamed spinach."

"Just a routine suppressor. Nothing to worry about. All no-therapy admissions receive suppressors. It makes for more uniform manageability."

"As long as I'm manageable."

"I don't think that you have very much to complain about. I reviewed the record of your stay, and you would seem to have been kept adequately amused." She held his eyes with a steady stare. For a moment, he thought that she was going to add a further remark. Instead, she moved briskly along. "You will be glad to hear that your companion, Adult Female A7, has made a full recovery from implant surgery."

"Does that mean we can leave here?"

"In a couple of days. She still needs rest."

"When can I see her?"

"Right now. In fact, she's asking for you. That's why I'm here."

Once again, she led Marlowe through the dim, black-walled corridors and up two levels in an elevator. When they arrived at Christine's room, the first thing that Marlowe noticed was that it was much larger and better-appointed than his.

"How are you?" he asked.

Christine nodded. "I'll live."

Carmila was already sitting on the bed beside her. Marlowe glanced pointedly at Kenwood and then looked back at Christine.

"Did everything go . . . according to plan?"

"You can talk in front of the doctor. They know what they did to me. All they don't know is why or who we are, although they've probably figured that out by now."

Kenwood looked a little uncomfortable. "Anonymity is always guaranteed."

"Of course it is."

Kenwood became very formal. "I have other calls to make."

Christine smiled sweetly. "Don't let me keep you."

"I'll leave the three of you together."

Once she was gone, Christine indicated that Marlowe should pull a chair up to the bed. "I'd sit down if I were you, Marlowe. You don't look too good."

"Did you really need to use my name?"

"What's done is done. There's no more need for secrecy. Anyone trying to probe me now will be wasting their time."

Carmila scowled. "And terminating yours."

"Stop worrying. Nobody is going to be that stupid." She turned her attention to Marlowe. "So what have they been doing to you Marlowe? You look like a zombie."

"They've been pumping me full of what they euphemistically call suppressors."

Carmila was less than sympathetic. "You should have done what I did and turned off the wallscreen."

"How did you know it was the wallscreen?"

"A couple of years ago, I was heavily into the recreational uses of alpha overload. Once you've tried it, you never forget the effect."

"If I'd turned off the screen, I probably would have gone mad with boredom. I think I'd rather have the suppressors."

"You probably don't have the concentration to do absolutely nothing."

Marlowe sighed. Once again he was playing Mutt to the two women's collective Jeff. "So where do we go from here?"

"They want to keep me here another couple of days. After that we need a protected place in which to hole up until the word has gone around that I can no longer be brainwashed or probed. After that, I can start to renegotiate my position. Dancer is already making the arrangements.''

Carmila pouted. ''I don't like Dancer.''

''Few people do. He's an obnoxious person. Fortunately, nobody has to like him. All that matters with Dancer is that he's completely loyal.''

Marlowe set the conversation back on what he saw as the track. ''What happens to me?''

''Once the supercorps accept the situation, you'll be in the clear. I'll set you up with some money, and you can go wherever you want.''

''As simple as that?''

''I don't want to adopt you, Marlowe.''

Marlowe remained confined to his room for the remaining two days, but the use of suppressors seemed to have ceased. He spent another hour with the woman in the old-fashioned nurse's uniform. Even without the suppressors the sense of unreality was almost as strong as it had been on the first occasion. He did decide, though, that with more time and a great deal of mental effort, he could probably turn the activity into an acceptable perversion.

The moment of his discharge finally came. Once again the talking head announced that Dr. Kenwood was on her way. Marlowe was gripped by a sudden impatience. He wanted to be out of it all. He wanted out of the clinic and out of the whole impossible deal. He didn't know exactly what he was going to do next. He knew that he would probably have to leave the Zone. Christine Stavers might be able to square things with the corporations and the police, but he doubted that she could do anything to call off Yorga. A blood feud with a vampire wasn't something that just went away. He supposed that he could move to Alphaville or Funtown. One leisure-out ghetto was much the same as another. But first he would have to slip back into town to retrieve his cat and salvage what might be left of the contents of his apartment.

When he arrived at the reception area, after a stop in the decontamination center to retrieve his freshly cleaned clothes, he found Christine, Carmila, Dancer, and four Stavers security men waiting for him. His impatience became a distinct nervousness—this was the final lap and he wanted to get through it without a last-minute disaster.

"Are we ready to move?" he asked.

Dancer nodded. "We've received a signal from the plane. It'll be here in a matter of minutes. We might as well start walking down to the landing pad."

Marlowe raised his hands in mock surprise. "You mean that's it? I'm free to go? I don't have to take a blood test or have a heart-to-heart chat with the warden?"

Christine shook her head. "I'm not sure I'm going to miss you, Marlowe."

"After all we've meant to each other?"

"Shall we go?"

The sky was overcast, so they heard the plane before they saw it. The sound of its engines changed as it began to drop on its downward thruster. The eight people beside the landing pad craned upward, peering into the cloud layer for a first glimpse. Then the Morgan jump jet emerged.

"What the hell does he think he's doing?" Dancer exclaimed.

The plane was slowly turning as it descended, almost as though it were looking for something.

"What the hell does he think he's flying, a military jet?"

Marlowe felt an unfocused fear creeping over him. Something was not right about that plane. Then he realized what was bothering him. "It's not like the one we came here in. There are no Stavers markings." In fact, it was just a plain white aircraft without even the normal commercial registration symbols.

The circular motion stopped. The jump jet was dropping smoothly now.

"It's going to land with the cabin door turned away from us," Carmila observed.

Dancer was already pulling out a gun. "I don't like this at all."

Marlowe, Christine, and Carmila instinctively took a few paces back, sheltering behind Dancer and the quartet of security men. The plane was about to touch. Its landing legs were only a meter or so from the ground when the violence erupted. The smoke came first. Whoever was inside must have opened the concealed cabin door and tossed out smoke grenades. The shock troops followed. Dark blue figures poured through the orange smoke, three and then three more, all in combat fatigues and full body armor. They hit the ground firing. Two of the Stavers security men went down in the first flurry.

"Oh, my god!"

Marlowe grabbed hold of Christine, pushing her in front of him. "Run!"

Another security man was down. Instead of going with Marlowe, Carmila darted forward and scooped up one of the weapons of a fallen man. More assault troops were coming around the nose and ducking under the plane. She loosed off a wild burst and then raced after Marlowe and Christine. Dancer was standing his ground and shooting from the hip. He got two of the blue-clad attackers before he, too, was cut down. Marlowe and Christine zigzagged in and out of the trees that lined the driveway. Carmila was a little behind them. At any moment, Marlowe expected bullets to be tearing into his back. Strangely, the gunfire seemed to have stopped. He risked glancing back. Eight or nine attackers were running up the drive after them, but they weren't using their weapons. Understanding came to him in a flash. Of course they weren't shooting. They had to take Christine alive. He moved closer to her. It had to be the safest place. They had reached the end of the drive and were almost to the courtyard. Three white-uniformed clinic guards were running in their direction. When the attackers saw them, they took them as a threat and started shooting. The men from the clinic immediately scattered, taking cover behind the monolith. Marlowe, Christine, and Carmila sprinted past them.

"Inside the main building!" Marlowe cried.

The glass doors opened automatically. The reception area was deserted. The three guards must have been on duty there.

"What do we do now?" Christine asked.

"This way. To the elevators."

The sound of gunfire came from the courtyard.

"Why elevators, Marlowe? Do you have a plan?"

"Not a plan. I just figure that we have to buy ourselves some time."

They were in the corridor that led to the elevator banks. A light came on and one set of doors opened. An orderly emerged, pushing a surgical trolley in front of him. Marlowe and Christine both careened into him. The trolley went over with a crash of glass and steel instruments. The orderly staggered sideways, staring at them in slack-jawed amazement. The elevator doors closed.

"How far down do we go?" Christine asked.

Marlowe touched the elevator control. "As far as we can."

The elevator started to drop, Christine leaned against the back wall, struggling to catch her breath. "I still don't see what you hope to achieve. There's nowhere to hide in a place like this. They're probably watching us right now."

Marlowe shrugged. "You got a better idea? It seems to me that we need any time we can get. You said you wanted to renegotiate your position, and it looks as if you're going to have to do it one hell of a lot faster than you ever imagined. You've got to get this new bunch of goons to realize the implications of that implant of yours."

For the first time, Marlowe saw Christine Stavers look really scared.

Carmila's expression was grim. "I want to know who sold us out. It was probably that bitch Kenwood."

"You don't know that."

The elevator stopped at the deepest level. The doors opened on a corridor that ran both left and right.

"So?" Christine said.

"Got a coin to flip?" Marlowe answered wryly.

"Go right," Carmila suggested.

They went right. The corridor was sunk in the same violet gloom as all the others that Marlowe had seen, and there didn't seem to be any way out except back into the elevator. The air there was cold and almost clammy. Marlowe was dreading the sound of the elevator doors opening. Pursuit couldn't be far behind.

"Maybe they don't use this level."

Marlowe glanced at Carmila and grunted. ''It's like the end of *The Third Man*.''

''The what?''

''Nothing.''

''What's that?'' she said, pointing.

Up ahead there was a break in the wall of the corridor.

''It's one of their containment locks,'' Marlowe replied.

When they reached it, Carmila inspected the access panel. ''It doesn't respond.''

''It's probably sealed.''

''So what do we do?''

A light on the panel suddenly came on.

''There must be someone on the other side coming out,'' Carmila guessed.

''Stand back,'' Marlowe said.

There was a hiss as an intake valve opened. Recalling all the movies he'd seen, Marlowe locked his hands together and raised them in readiness. The outer door slid open. An orderly stepped out humming an unrecognizable tune. Marlowe brought his hands down as hard as he could, right behind the orderly's ear. She folded and dropped. Marlowe could scarcely believe his success, but there was no time to preen.

''Grab the door!''

''Too late!''

The lock had resealed itself. When she'd fallen, the orderly had dropped a pencil-sized instigator identical to the one Kenwood had used to open the door to his room. He snatched it up and pressed it to a pad on the door panel. The door opened. They stepped into the lock. There was just enough room for the three of them. The door closed behind them and there was a soft hissing as the air was exchanged. The inner door slid back.

''Jesus Christ!''

They were stepping into a huge, dimly lit open area that reminded Marlowe of a barn. The air inside was considerably warmer. The source of the warmth was immediately apparent. The place was filled with people. There had to be over a hundred naked humans in the area. Maybe more. It was hard to tell, for the violet-tinged lighting was only marginally brighter than that in the corridor.

"What the hell are these supposed to be?" Marlowe asked.

Carmila calmly surveyed the scene. "They have to be spare-part clones."

"Dear God!"

The naked humans were all young adults, both male and female, seeming healthy teenagers, but with totally blank faces and the vacant stare of the wholly mindless. Filament-thin, green laser beams sectioned them by threes and fours into what amounted to pens. Some sat, others stood, while still more shuffled aimlessly. The only time they showed even the slightest animation was when one accidentally touched a laser beam. Then there would be a snap and a flash, and the human would recoil, making small mewing sounds.

"How did they get like this?"

"They breed them like this. Their sole purpose is to provide replacement organs."

Carmila seemed quite unfazed by the spectacle. Marlowe felt a little sick.

"Is this legal?" he asked.

"Probably not. The Lance-Koch Act was supposed to outlaw this kind of cloning, but it was so badly drafted that no one ever prosecutes. The case would probably be in court for twenty years. Nobody's got the money to go up against the medicorps."

Marlowe didn't want to know how Carmila knew so much about spare-part cloning. They were walking down a central aisle between the laser pens, and Marlowe was close to being spooked by the lines of blank faces. Some had even been born without eyes.

"They're complete vegetables, right?"

"That's the story."

"But they are, aren't they? They don't really know what's happening, do they?"

"What do you think?"

"And they're born that way?"

"That's also the story. Although there have been rumors about how, when the cloning doesn't come out right, there's quite a bit of fetal surgery."

Marlowe shook his head. "I'm damned if I know."

"Look at it this way, Marlowe. It's better like this than the way it was before. At least, hundreds of vags and nonpeople aren't vanishing every year."

Christine sniffed. "I heard that the only reason the clinics stopped using vags for spares was that the danger of disease got too great."

They were approaching the other end of the area. The pens were coming to an end. Modular containers, which probably held whatever slop was fed to these inhuman things, were stacked up against the rear wall. Marlowe halted.

"I think this is the end of the road. What we should do is hole up behind these units and see what happens next. At least we've got a weapon."

Carmila dourly hefted the machine pistol. "We only have one clip."

"You want to give me that?"

Carmila glared at Marlowe. "Why? You still think killing's men's work?"

Marlowe shrugged. "So keep the piece. I was hoping we could avoid any more killing."

They crawled in among the containers. Each found a position where they could see out but not be seen. They smelled something like rotting vegetation—whatever was in the containers had leaked out around the valves.

"What are we supposed to do, Marlowe? Just wait?"

"I think someone will be along very soon."

It didn't take long for Marlowe to be proved right. The containment lock opened and people started coming through in threes. At first, it was only the clinic guards in their distinctive white uniforms, but then three of the men in dark blue combat fatigues emerged. Marlowe cursed under his breath. Obviously, despite the gunfire out in the courtyard, the clinic and the unidentified intruders had come to some sort of understanding.

A line of armed men was forming in front of the containment lock. Someone turned off the laser pens. The clones began to stir uneasily. The line moved forward, herding the clones to the sides as it advanced. There were grunts and some guttural bellows. Carmila was aiming her weapon. She looked at Marlowe questioningly.

He shook his head. "Just a warning burst."

Carmila took her time. She waited until the line was almost two thirds of the way down the area before she cut loose with the machine pistol. The bullets went over the men's heads, but only just. The clones set up an immediate clamor. The line halted. Marlowe heard Christine hissing at him.

"Say something, for Christ's sake."

Marlowe cupped hands in front of his mouth. "Stay where you are! We don't want to hurt anybody!"

There was a small knot of medical people back by the containment lock. A woman detached herself and hurried toward the line. Marlowe recognized Kenwood.

Carmila's face contorted into a snarl. "I ought to waste the bitch."

"Don't you dare."

Kenwood slipped through the line and walked slowly toward the stack of containers. Carmila raised her gun.

"That's far enough."

"There's no way that you can get out of here."

Marlowe took over. "What's going on, Dr. Kenwood? Why are your people helping our kidnappers? We're being snatched from right inside your clinic, goddamn it. You let that happen to your patients?"

"These people are properly bonded operatives under contract to the RAMco conglomerate. They have properly constituted warrants for the three of you, all signed by a judge. We have to turn you over to them; our hands are tied." She spread her hands, palms outward in a reverse confirmation of her final remark. "Besides, you aren't patients. You'd already been discharged."

Marlowe looked at Christine. "It seems like we're screwed."

"The hell we are." She shouted down to Kenwood. "Did you tell these properly bonded operatives why I was here? Did you tell them about the operation?"

"They have been made aware of the implant."

"Damn it, woman, don't you ever speak English? These goons are going to take me out of here and probe my mind. You know what will happen to me?"

"I have their assurance that you won't be harmed."

''What about those of my people they've already shot? Don't you call that harm?''

''There's nothing that I can do to help you, Ms. Stavers.''

Carmila was muttering obscenities. Marlowe looked at the two women.

''So we have two choices: We either try and make a fight of it with one clip of ammunition or we come out with our hands in the air.''

They both stared at him in silence. Neither wanted to be the one to say it. Marlowe sighed. He slowly stood up and raised his hands.

''Okay. We're coming out. Don't shoot.''

EIGHT

IF ANYTHING, IT WAS EVEN MORE ANTISEPTIC THAN THE Sheila McKenna Clinic. This was a technocrat cathedral in glass, stainless steel, and soaring, unbroken sheets of white plastone. Its design function was to dwarf man with his own achievements. Such a combination of humility and blatantly meglo self-aggrandizement could only be the product of what Jenner had defined as the advanced corporate psyche. It must have been a full hundred feet from the floor to the vaulted, carbon-glass roof, but this, and the other three transfer concourses, were only footnotes to the kilometer-tall control spire. That was the tallest freestanding structure on the planet. It wasn't any consolation to Marlowe that the grandeur through which he was being transported was the product of something that history would define as a monumental collective madness. Right at that moment, Marlowe wasn't sure if there was going to be any history, at least as far as he was concerned. He had become so sick with fear that he was virtually walking in a daze.

If there was any consolation at all, and Marlowe wasn't at all convinced that there was, nothing was going as he had imagined. He had half expected that once he was in the hands of the RAMco goons, he would be whisked away to some concrete-walled sub-basement with bright lights, clamps, electrodes, and steel dog whips. In fact, his captors had been nothing worse than coldly cordial. Coffee had been offered once the plane was in the air, although he, Christine, and Carmila had declined. One of the men in blue combat fatigues even brought out a pack of Kenyan Luckies, an offer Marlowe gratefully accepted. Beyond these pleasantries there was no contact. No questions were answered and all conversations were terminated with a standard phrase: ''I'm not cleared to discuss that with you, sir.''

The flight had droned on in silence that was only broken by muttered, half-heard remarks and muffled guffaws on the part of the RAMco men. The pilot's announcement that they were starting their descent to the Lovelock Space Center had come as a complete surprise. As the impossibly tall, tapering spire became visible on the right-hand side of the aircraft, Marlowe and Christine had exchanged glances. There was a certain logic to their being brought there: It was the largest of the RAMco installations and, as such, it was the hub of the corporation's considerable empire. The problem was one of style. There was something wrong about the choice of destination. The space center was too noble, too dedicated to its purpose. This was where the big payload ships rode their boosters up through the atmosphere or glided back to Earth with their airfoils extended. It was the corporation's stepping-stone to the stars, the bottom of the great gravity well. Even the architecture demonstrated the purity of vision and purpose. It was hardly the kind of place that came equipped with secret rooms where a woman might have her brain opened or a leisure-out could be quietly lost forever. The only other explanation was that they were being taken into space—and that was patently absurd.

The jump jet dropped to a thoroughly normal executive-vehicle landing pad where a black limousine was waiting. The three captives were handed over to a half-dozen representatives of regular RAMco security, young men of exactly the same type as the Stavers security people who had taken them to the clinic. RAMco's security wore tan suits with nehru collars and were no more communicative than the troops who had accompanied the captives on the plane.

The limousine took them through an underground internal road system to the Number Three Transfer Concourse. After a fifteen-minute drive, the long black car nosed its way into a basement car park where they were let off and surrounded by a phalanx of security men who took them up to the main floor level. Once there, they headed directly for the elevators that gave access to the towering control spire. Crossing the main floor of the complex, Marlowe, Christine, and Carmila found themselves back in the realm of the general public, or at least as general a public as it could be when its single bond was that it ventured into space to the moon base or the orbital environments. The three prisoners and their escort drew a number of curious glances, but there was nothing about the crowd on the concourse that gave Marlowe the slightest hope that it would provide him with any sort of cover in the unlikely event that he was able to break away from the security men.

The concourse was peopled by pretty much the kind of characters that television had led Marlowe to expect would be at a space port. There were a few well-dressed, clearly wealthy types, the ones who had the money to buy passage into space simply for the experience. By far the majority were the rank and file of the space industry, the ones who actually manned and constructed the bases and the environments. In total contrast to the well-dressed, wealthy clientele and the immaculate ground staff and security, the trend among the offworld roustabouts was toward a high level of funk. Patch-decorated coveralls, duck-billed caps, utility vests with mazes of flaps and pockets, and bulky moon boots were the order of the day. Quite a few walked with the weary, bent-knee, round-shouldered gait of those who have just come back from low or zero gravity. In many respects they were very similar to the pioneers of the past, the oil-field roughnecks of the previous century, or the trailblazers who had opened up the American continent a hundred years earlier.

The new arrivals had to pass no less than four checkpoints before they could ride one of the elevators that ran up the control spire. It was one of those glassed-in, external elevators that was supposed to give a breathtaking panoramic view but all too often simply caused extreme anxiety. Marlowe, who disliked being exposed to heights even in films, hated the whole idea, but even he had to admit that the view they had from the thirtieth floor of a Prometheus-class shuttle rising into the sky on a pillar of smoke and flame, while the whole Earth seemed to tremble, was nothing short of magnificent. The sun was starting to set over the high desert in a copper-gold haze. It invested the landscape that stretched in front of them with a soft-focus, parchment magic. The blast pits and the spaces between the hangars and the other structures were filled with dark shadows. Lights were starting to come on. The huge launch gantries stood black against the reddening sky like the scaffolds of the gods. When they reached the fourty-fifth floor, it was just possible to see, through the haze, in the far distance, the bulk of the IKG ziggurat, like some man-made mesa out on the horizon. Marlowe had never been able to understand why these two major space centers had been built within just a few miles of each other. It was like some crazed, original joke on the part of whoever had given out the initial land grants, condemning these two corporate titans to glower at each other from their respective towers like jealous feudal warlords.

At the fifty-second floor, the elevator came to a halt and they found themselves in a clean, white corporate corridor. Executive personnel in formal dark suits and officers of the flight division in sky-blue uniforms went about their business. The sprinkling of darker air-force blue had to be an attempt to reinforce the fiction that there was still a federal involvement in the development of outer space. Marlowe, Carmila, and Christine were ushered into a perfectly ordinary conference room with a long walnut table, eight leather chairs, a RAMco flag on a brass staff, and framed photographs of various models of spacecraft. Beyond the wide picture window, the sky was purple and the base was coming to nighttime life. Two security men took up positions on either side of the door while the rest filed out. Marlowe suspected they wouldn't be far away if he took it into his head to cause trouble. A perky secretary came in and smiled at them.

"Mr. Castilio will be with you in just a few minutes."

"Who's Castilio?"

"Is there anything that you need? Coffee, maybe?"

Marlowe spoke for the three of them. "We don't want any coffee. We want to know under what authority we're being detained and when we'll be released."

"Mr. Castilio will be with you in just a few minutes."

Castilio was a hard-eyed cal-hispanic. He looked like the kind who had probably entered the corporation through a PEI lottery and then clawed up every inch of the hard way by his fingernails. His taste still leaned in the direction of street machismo. From the greased curls of his pompadour, through the slick sharkskin drape, to the overly pointed shoes, he was nothing less than the executive version of the pachuco greez.

"Please be seated."

His voice was a soft rasp. Marlowe knew instinctively that they could expect no favors from this one. On his way to the fifty-second floor, carrying the weight of PEI street-trash stigma but still trashing the supercilious Harvard Business School bastards, he must have become ultimately cold. He might even be a throwback to Central America in its death-squad days. The three sat, but they were less than comfortable. Castilio shot a pair of long white cuffs. The links were gold crucifixes. There was an Order of Conquistadors ring on the pinky of his left hand.

"I hope you haven't been caused too much inconvenience."

Christine bristled. "We've been kidnapped. How much more inconvenient can it get?"

"You could be dead."

Marlowe hadn't expected Castilio to show his teeth quite so soon. "I guess that's the bottom line," he said.

"Indeed it is."

Christine didn't see it that way. "Are you threatening me?"

"Not at all, Ms. Stavers. I'm just stating a fact."

"And what about the fact that your corporation has totally violated my civil rights? That's hardly normal treatment of the major shareholder of another corporation."

"I assure you that our actions have been completely legal."

Marlowe scowled. "How do you figure that?"

"Perhaps we should review your position. For some time now, RAMco and the minority shareholders of Stavers Industries have been attempting to complete a benign merger. Your opposition to that merger has been increasingly irrational. On evidence of your recent unstable behavior, we could only conclude that you were no longer legally capable and we presented our case to a federal judge. He granted a temporary decree of incompetence, which permitted us to detain you and hold you for a full psychiatric evaluation."

"You know that's bullshit. Everyone has a judge in his pocket."

"Nevertheless, it's completely legal bullshit."

Christine took a deep breath. "And does this psychiatric evaluation include mind probe?"

Castilio smiled like an affable shark. "That is not my department. I'm basically a lawyer."

Marlowe sighed. "I should have known."

Christine leaned toward Castilio. "Do you know what will happen if you attempt to mind probe me?"

"We're examining the reports from the McKenna clinic."

"And?"

"I think we have to get one thing straight, Ms. Stavers. I'm not here to in any way negotiate with you. This is just a preliminary interview. Nothing will be decided in your case until you are safely aboard the orbital environment."

Marlowe's jaw dropped. "The what?"

"The orbital environment, Mr. Marlowe. To discourage any ill-advised rescue attempts, the three of you will be transferred to the RAMco orbital environment."

"I'm not going into space. Forget it. You might as well shoot me now."

"You're scared, Marlowe?"

"Damn right I'm scared."

Castilio seemed amused. "I assure you that space flight is safer than most forms of ground transportation."

"Oh yeah? What about the *Challenger*? The *Kingfisher*? The *Leningrad*? The *Buckley*?"

"You might as well say what about the *Titanic*. It's all irrelevant, Marlowe. You people are much too disruptive to remain on-world. You're going up to the environment. That is also not negotiable."

Marlowe wished he could retreat into catatonia. His worst fears seemed to be standing on-line, waiting to get him.

Castilio looked from Carmila to Marlowe to Christine. "Does anyone have anything else to say?"

Christine nodded. "You'd better give maximum priority to reading those reports from McKenna. If anyone starts to screw around with my head, you lose everything."

"Believe me, Ms. Stavers, you are going to be treated with the most—" He smiled. "—intensive care. Is there anything else?"

Christine shook her head. "Just read the goddamn report."

Castilio spoke into thin air. "Ms. Adler, please send in the nurse."

The relentlessly perky secretary must have been monitoring the conversation, Marlowe realized.

"What do we need a nurse for?" he asked.

"You're going to be medicated. It's against corporation policy for unwilling passengers to be conscious during the burn up the well."

The door opened and a nurse walked in carrying a foil-sealed tray. She was backed up by two more security men. She pulled the tag on the foil. There was a faint hiss as the vacuum seal was broken. The tray contained three disposable syrosols.

"Please roll your sleeve up, Mr. Marlowe."

Marlowe hesitated. Was he going to go to the gas chamber with dignity, or kicking and screaming? He took a deep breath and rolled up his sleeve. The nurse placed the syrosol against the inside of his elbow. There was a pricking sensation as the medication microblasted through his skin. The nurse was moving on to Carmila. Nothing was happening to Marlowe. There was something wrong with the injection. He wasn't going under.

And then Marlowe was in a bare white room.

It wasn't in the least like waking from sleep. Subjectively, no time had elapsed and yet he was somewhere else. The only indication that he had been out at all was a rapidly disintegrating dreamscape of canyons, naked people without faces, and a roaring volcano. If he tried to focus on it, however, the vision simply melted away.

"Good day, Marlowe. I'm happy to perceive that you are awake." The voice came from nowhere. Computer-generated and approximately female, it was set roughly halfway between comforting and seductive.

"Where am I?"

"You are a guest in the Delta 7 holding facility."

"I'm in space?"

"The final frontier."

"My god."

He slowly turned his head. He was gripped by an irrational fear that any sudden move would result in disaster. The room was little more than a cubicle, just large enough to accommodate the bunk on which he lay. The walls were covered in some kind of soft white plastic. It made for an uncomfortable resemblance to a padded cell. There was a narrow door, but it was without a handle or any other means of opening it. There was also a smaller panel in the opposite wall but absolutely no indication as to its purpose. In many respects it was like being back at the McKenna clinic, except there he had been given a kimono, and here he was naked. A loose net of blue webbing secured him to the bunk.

"Why am I tied down?"

"It's standard procedure. Although the Delta area is located in a rotating section of the environment where centrifugal force stimulates point seven Earthside gravity, experienced offworlders still strap in to sleep in case of a malfunction. It also tends to create a sense of security."

"How do I get out of this thing?"

Marlowe was trying to figure out where the hidden speakers were. The voice seemed to come from the exact center of the room.

"If you run your hand along the outside of the bunk frame you will find a recessed button. When you press it, the webbing will unhook and retract into the wall. Please do not do this yet. There are some things that you should know.''

''There are?''

''You are in point seven Earthside gravity and you have no experience of it. Your coordination will be off by some thirty percent. Try to compensate accordingly and do not over physicalize.''

''Can I hit the button now?''

''Go ahead.''

The webbing unlocked and slithered back into a slot in the wall. Marlowe sat up. The movement made him feel a little dizzy. He swung his legs over the side of the bunk. After a slight hesitation, he put his feet down on the floor and tried to stand. The floor was covered in fibrous matting. It must have provided a grip surface for Velcro-soled slippers. He could only assume that there had once been a time when this part of the environment had not rotated to generate its own gravity. On the first attempt, he stumbled forward for a couple of paces and had to grab the wall to steady himself. He was experiencing a giddy lightheadedness that wasn't particularly pleasant. Part of him was considering throwing up.

''I don't feel so good.''

''It will pass. Acclimation is very rapid.''

''How would you know?''

''I know everything.''

The damn thing had a secondary humor response program. Marlowe hated humor programs—they reminded him of the drunk at the party who's the only one in the room who thinks he's funny. He experimented with walking. Unfortunately, it took just two and a half paces to travel the length of the cubicle, so he didn't have a great deal of scope, but even in these limited conditions he quickly got the hang of it, except that he couldn't quite correct a tendency to bounce.

''I am cleared to uncover the port for your first view of space. Do you wish me to do that?''

''I . . .'' Marlowe really didn't know. Once he looked out at the void, there would be no way to pretend that he wasn't really there. He was far from certain that he was ready to deal with the void, but he decided that there was no way that he could delay it. "Yeah, okay, open it up."

The wall panel folded back. Marlowe leaned forward and peered out.

"Goddamn!" His voice was a whisper. The word *awesome* had become so debased that it didn't even start to describe what he was seeing. He was staring into infinity. "I never knew there were so many stars."

"In this section, the ports are turned away from the Earth. That is unfortunate. The planet is considered a magnificent spectacle."

A half-dismantled payload rocket floated past the port. Tiny figures in space suits swarmed over it. There was the flash of cutting lasers and arc guns. The rocket seemed to be moving in a strangely curving flight.

"Remember that the section is rotating and this accounts for the apparent movement of nearby objects," the voice told him.

Something else had come into view. Five deep-space tugs were towing a massive, roughly spherical chunk of dark rock. Four robot drones maneuvered something that looked like a huge silver parasol; it seemed to be shielding the sunward side of the rock mass. As it was towed along, the rock left a rapidly dispersing trail of snowlike debris as if it were gradually disintegrating.

"What the hell is that?"

"They're bringing in a small ice asteroid. It will be cut up and fed into the crusher and then piped to the filtration plant where it will be converted into usable water. The tugs belong to independent ice prospectors operating under license. Ice prospecting is an optimum-growth industry. The burn cost of bringing up water from the planet is, with no pun intended, astronomical."

The port started to darken.

"What's happening?"

"The section is turning into the sun. The ports are coated to opaque-out in direct sunlight."

When the sun had passed, the port cleared again. The payload rocket was coming around for a second time. It was easy for Marlowe to adjust to the space station's rotation once it had been explained. He wasn't, however, given much more time to get used to the view. As the payload rocket drifted from sight, the door to the cubicle silently opened.

"Close the port, please," a new voice said.

Marlowe spun around. A figure in a black and gray jumpsuit with a silver insignia was standing in the entrance. A second figure, in an identical uniform, waited outside. The ensembles were completed by triangular forage caps and dark glasses. A club and a stun gun hung from each of their belts. The figure in the doorway studied Marlowe as if he were a specimen. Marlowe instinctively covered his genitals with his hands. He wished he could see the man's eyes. He felt completely exposed.

"What is this?"

"You will come with us."

"Like this? I don't get any clothes?"

The man held out a flat, plastic-wrapped package. "Put this on."

Marlowe avoided the cold, impassive stare of the dark glasses as he tore off the wrapper. Inside was a shapeless, one-piece white garment made of woven paper fiber. Marlowe held it up in disgust. "You expect me to wear paper clothes?"

"Put it on, Marlowe. You only get real clothes if and when you're released from detention."

"But paper clothes . . ."

The man put a hand on his club. "Something you should understand is that here in Delta section you do what you're told—without question."

The gesture wasn't wasted on Marlowe. He quickly started pulling on the paper coverall. The legs were too long and he had to roll them up in order to be able to walk. As he fastened it he glanced up at the figure in the doorway. "What are you people, anyway?"

"I'm Officer Burns, and behind me is Officer Koto. We're both Installation Police. Are you ready to move?"

"I guess so."

As he was marched through the installation, Marlowe became very aware that he was walking inside the rim of a massive wheel. The illusion was one of being in the bottom of a perpetual dip with the floor always curving upward both in front and behind. There was a strange feeling of not really getting anywhere, like a hamster on a treadmill. The illusion would have been even more intense if the companionway along which they were walking hadn't been divided into short, twenty-meter sections by sets of airtight doors.

"Where are we going?"

"Shut up, Marlowe. You'll find out soon enough."

The room was gray steel with black trim. The desk looked like a single block of black glass. One wall was covered with a complex of infrared monitor screens that showed what was taking place in various parts of the installation. The screens showed the interiors of rooms and corridors and external views of construction. One screen, slightly to the left of the center, showed what appeared to be a highly pornographic orgy in progress. The man behind the desk was squat and florid, with carrot-red hair. His eyes were light blue and mean, with pale lashes. From the insignia on his police jumpsuit, he clearly outranked Burns and Koto by a number of grades. His fingers danced over a touch panel set in the desktop as Marlowe was ushered into the room. The varied images vanished and were replaced by the same live closeup of Marlowe's face repeated on every screen. The effect of seeing himself so multiplied was highly intimidating. Insult was added to intimidation by the fact that he looked so awful. During the time that he'd been drugged, his beard had grown out to a dark stubble and there were deep circles under his eyes. He looked like a prisoner. Without thinking, he pushed his hands through his hair. The cop behind the desk smiled briefly at this unconscious vanity.

"Marlowe." It was a statement, not a question and instinct told Marlowe not to answer. "I hope you haven't suffered any ill effects."

Marlowe shook his head. "Not that I've noticed."

The cop nodded. "That's good."

His fingers moved briefly over the touch panel again. A single, still picture of Christine Stavers appeared on the center screen. It had the stark brutality of a police mug shot and it must have been taken since they had been brought into space.

"She's not being particularly cooperative."

"She never is."

"How about you, Marlowe? Are you cooperative?"

"Always. I like a quiet life."

"You don't seem to be particularly successful at it."

"It was cooperating that got me into this mess."

"You've been cooperating with the wrong people."

"It's starting to look that way."

"Fortunately, your cooperation isn't my direct concern."

There didn't seem to be any answer to that, so again Marlowe kept quiet. He had a feeling that he was being softened up for something. The red-haired cop hit the touches again and Christine vanished.

"I'm De Kuyper and I'm supervisor of police on this installation."

Marlowe waited to see what was coming next.

"My only function, as far as you're concerned, is to explain some of the facts of life."

Again Marlowe waited.

"You're in space, Marlowe."

"I'm very aware of that."

"But you don't know what that means."

"I don't?"

"Probably no more than your friend Stavers. She keeps talking about her rights and how she wants to negotiate or how she wants to talk to some lawyer back on Earth. She hasn't realized yet that we're not on Earth anymore. All that is behind us. This is space, Marlowe. The old rules don't apply. Look at this, Marlowe."

He hit the touches yet again. A port cover almost the size of the whole wall behind the desk began to fold back. Once again *awesome* was a completely inadequate word. The port looked down the entire length of the environment. It must have been a full two kilometers to the other end. Below it was the curved horizon of the Earth. The environment was complex in the extreme. It was basically a set of parallel wheels linked by a trunklike central hub. Small wheel sections were set out at the end of long single spokes like spidery towers. There were also the more squat projections of container booms and the needle points of docking pylons.

"This is another world, Marlowe, and we are the aliens."

Marlowe could do nothing but stare. The rest of the roughly cylindrical megastructure didn't rotate along with the section they were in, so he could only suppose that the bulk of the installation was without simulated gravity. Much of it was still under construction. Directly below them, space-suited welders were attaching outer skin plates to the underlying girderwork. There were large areas of unfinished framework. Many of them were festooned with straggles of shapeless placbag tubing which, although Marlowe didn't know it at the time, were temporary housing for the rocket trash. Small craft, some towing strings of container modules, floated in and out of a half-dozen ports or moved across the surface of the station. Marlowe was reminded of a giant beehive with workers swarming over it. Despite its overwhelming size Marlowe couldn't help but sense that there was something piecemeal about it, as though it had been put together in stages rather than according to a single master design. In that, it was something akin to a city. Some distance to the right, a streamlined shuttle craft was getting underway in a flare of rocket exhaust. The main environment wasn't alone in space; two smaller installations, which looked like industrial plants, stood off in syncronized orbits.

"Look at the planet, Marlowe."

The Earth was blue-green and streaked with wispy cloud masses.

"It looks clean and serene from here, doesn't it? Don't be deceived. It's diseased and dying. The seas and the atmosphere are tainted beyond any reclamation. It may linger for a while, but the process is irreversible." De Kuyper's eyes flashed for an instant. Obviously the police chief had a vision, and Marlowe had always made it a rule to steer clear of men with visions. "We are the only hope that humanity has. We've fouled our planet, but here in space we have a second chance. We will not make the same mistakes again, and nothing will be allowed to get in our way. Do you understand me, Marlowe?"

"I'm beginning to."

"Out here, the old rules don't apply any longer. You might say that it was the old rules and the old ways that destroyed the planet. In space, it's a clean slate. We're very determined people, Marlowe. It's bigger even than RAMco. The groundside corporations are nothing but stepping-stones. We are the future, and nothing or nobody is going to threaten that future."

A minute earlier, Marlowe wouldn't have believed himself capable of a greater fear, but the realization that he was in the hands of a fanatic dumped him into some new sub-basement of desperation.

"How do I convince you people that I'm not a threat of any kind? I got into this mess by mistake and all I want is to get out of it."

"We don't know what you are or what you want, but we intend to find out."

"What's that supposed to mean?"

"You're going to room 101 on the outer hub for routine interrogation and probe. After that, Director Raxalt will decide what's going to be done with you. You'd better be telling the truth, Marlowe."

Marlowe's stomach had turned to ice. This couldn't be happening to him. De Kuyper was summoning an escort.

Room 101 was divided into two distinct sections by a floor-to-ceiling Plexiglas screen. On one side there was a small control room, a shadowy place full of multicolored leds flashing pinpoints of light. There was just room for two operator's chairs between the complex control board and the banks of nameless outboard hardware. The other side was a complete and sinister contrast—a brightly lit chamber. The walls were covered in the same soft plastic as the room in which he'd woken. The focal point of the chamber was a high-backed steel and plastic chair with some particularly malignant stim feeders built into the back, the arms, and the headrest. It might have belonged to a dentist who didn't care particularly for his patients' peace of mind. It also looked a lot like some high-tech version of the twentieth-century electric chair—and that didn't do much for Marlowe's peace of mind.

Room 101 was the domain of a small, balding, pear-shaped man called Murphy. He went about his work with a bad-tempered efficiency that involved his constant complaining to himself. His particular beef of the moment seemed to be the unreasonable demands of his workload.

"I keep telling them that I can't be expected to do four

in a day if they're going to be done properly. Please remove your garment."

Marlowe hesitated.

Murphy sighed. "This is nothing personal, but please hurry it up. I have a very tight schedule."

Marlowe pulled off the paper coverall.

"Now sit in the chair, please."

Marlowe eased himself into the chair. There was a RAMco logo on the headrest. The plastic was cold against his skin. He had lapsed into a state of dull shock—it was the simplest form of protective detachment. He was a long way away, and all this was happening to somebody else. Murphy was securing him in the chair with plastic webbing restraints.

"Do you have any implanted receptors?"

"No." His voice sounded strange.

Murphy pursed his lips. "It's as though all of you dirtsiders were stimmed out of your minds all the time."

"Not me."

"I'll have to put a temporary in the back of your neck. Please incline your head."

Something that looked like an oversized syrosol was placed against the base of Marlowe's skull. There was a hiss. His skin had gone numb, but he was very aware that a foreign object was sticking in his flesh. Murphy attached a stim line to it. For almost five minutes, he busied himself hooking clips, clamps, and contact points to various parts of Marlowe's body, keeping up a constant disgruntled patter. Finally he stepped back and inspected his work. He seemed satisfied.

"I guess that'll do. I'll just seal you in the headpiece and we'll be ready to run the program. Like I said, it's nothing personal."

Marlowe couldn't believe that the man could be so matter-of-fact about something that was little more than sophisticated torture. Maybe the guys who had operated the rack and the thumbscrews had been just the same. Marlowe's fear turned to churning panic when Murphy placed black adhesive pads over his eyes. He could no longer see. Some kind of metal helmet was being lowered over his head. For stretched, agonizing seconds, nothing happened. When the voice came, it was right inside his head.

"Please try and relax." It was the same damn voice, the soft quasi-female voice that had talked to him when he had first woken up in space. "In this first phase, your system will be flooded with disinhibitors of increasing strength. You will feel no discomfort whatsoever. The pain will not come until the second phase."

Marlowe would have been more than happy to have had that information kept from him. The disinhibitors were already kicking in and he was slipping down into a warm, comfortable torpor.

"You are now ready for the second phase."

Marlowe thought that he could feel sweat running down his face, but he wasn't sure. Small, stabbing pains started in the back of his neck and ran down his spine. He twisted slightly in the chair, but the restraints held him fast.

"From this point on, the discomfort will increase in stages. Please bear in mind that whatever you suffer will be strictly subjective and that you are in no danger of permanent physiological damage. There is, on the other hand, a considerable risk of psychological scarring if you attempt to willfully resist the program, or if you fail to give full and sincere responses to the questions that will be asked."

Marlowe wished that he could get away from the voice. There was now a hideous edge to the pseudosexy, reassuring purr.

"Tell us about yourself, Marlowe."

What kind of interrogation was this? "There really isn't that much to tell."

Blinding white pain sliced up through his spine and sent waves of shock out to his fingers and all the way down to his toes. Inside his helmet, his own scream was deafening.

"We aren't playing games, Marlowe. Please tell us about yourself in your own terms. You may begin anywhere."

Marlowe launched into a halting account of his life and his background. The pain had been reduced to minor stabbings in the nerve clusters in his neck and shoulders. Now and again it would rise in intensity, either to urge him along or to nudge him in a specific direction. The voice would ask the odd direct question, but for the most part, he was allowed to ramble. Marlowe lost track of how long the virtual monologue had gone on. All he knew was that he seemed to be acquiring a certain skill at avoiding the shocks. It was almost as though the machine had suckered him in. Just as he was telling himself that this wasn't going to be as bad as he had imagined, three shocks hit him without the slightest warning. They were worse than anything that had gone before. Once again he was deafened by his own screaming.

"It's time for you to go deeper."

This time the pain didn't abate. The shocks came one after the other. Blood-red, not-quite-defined hallucinations lurked in the periphery of his vision.

"I . . . can't! I don't . . . know what . . . you mean!"

"Go deeper."

"What do you mean . . . deeper?"

"We want to get to know you, Marlowe. Go deeper inside yourself. Start wherever you like. Tell us about those little things that you've always concealed."

Marlowe entered a period of agony and confession. As the pain wrung his nervous system, he sobbed out all the tiny, shameful secrets from childhood up. Things came out of his mind that he wasn't even aware that he remembered. Nothing was too petty or too nasty. All he wanted was to please the voice and stop the torment. He loved the voice and wanted only to please it. Whenever a question was asked, he seized on it like an anxious puppy fetching a rubber bone. The pain didn't recede, but there came a point when he seemed to be apart from it. He was a small child moving around inside his own mind, sampling memories of his childhood. It was as if he were inside some huge library and everything he knew was contained in the hundreds of dusty books on its shelves. The hallucinations had coalesced into vague demon forms and now lurked at the ends of the stacks, ready to get him if he hesitated or made an error. The questions came more frequently, easing him toward what he knew about Christine and Stavers Industries. Some of the questions were exceedingly technical and quite beyond him. The demons kept closing in and ripping at his flesh. He was being punished simply because he didn't have the answers. He felt that he was suffocating.

"For god's sake. I . . . can't tell you what I don't know."

He wanted to answer. He truly wanted the voice to know everything, but nobody had told him anything about access codes or retrieval procedures.

"I believe you, Marlowe. I believe you."

Blackness was folding around him like a velvet shroud. The pain had stopped. He was slowly sinking into something warm and soft.

"I believe you, Marlowe. I believe you."

The next thing he knew he was back in the white cell where he had first woken, or one exactly like it. He was naked and strapped down to the bunk. He expected to be in pain, but he wasn't. The interrogation had left no lasting effects apart from a stiffness in his joints, a feeling that his brain had turned to mush, and a difficulty in focusing his eyes. When he finally spoke out loud, his voice was low and tentative.

"Is there anybody there?"

There was no answer. Marlowe was desolate. He wanted the voice to come and comfort him. He wanted the voice to love him.

"Somebody talk to me."

Nobody did. He lay still for a while longer. He seemed to have been stripped of all independent will. Maybe a half hour went by—Marlowe had no means of telling. He decided he had to try to get a grip on himself. He moved an exploratory hand along the edge of the bunk looking for the button that would release the webbing holding him down. His fingers touched it, and the webbing slid back into its recess. He tried to sit up and found the action not at all difficult. Standing took a little longer. His legs felt like jelly and tended to tremble. He was also inexplicably hungry, and his throat felt as though it had been blowtorched.

"Anybody out there?"

He couldn't believe that after all he'd been through they were just going to leave him in this cell to die of thirst.

After what felt like another half hour, the door opened

and a pair of black-and-gray-uniformed cops were standing there.

"It's about time you were awake, Marlowe."

"It is?"

"You've been out for forty-eight hours."

"I have?"

"Time for you to come with us."

The whole thing was starting all over again. Marlowe had an urge to start screaming and never stop, but he put a brake on it. The interrogation had to have been the worst. What else could they do to him? They must be satisfied by now that he was a know-nothing asshole.

"Where are we going?"

"You're going right to the top, Marlowe. You have an audience with the director."

"Do I do any better than the paper suit?"

The cop held one out.

"For an audience with the director? I thought he was the big cheese around here. He doesn't rate real clothes?"

"Just put it on."

The director's suite was an opulent waste of space in an environment where space was at a claustrophobic premium, occupying a flying bridge on the inside rim of the rotating section. One wall and half the roof were a clear plastic shell. The sun was on the other side of the installation, and a panorama of the cosmos rolled endlessly past. The area under the Plexiglas was dominated by a smoke-gray plastic block that could have been the coffin of a giant. It served as part desk and part primary control station. The top, which was tilted slightly forward, had at least two dozen screens built into it along with banks of touch boards. In total contrast, a single red rose in a champagne flute had been placed on one of the desk's flat surfaces. The desk was flanked by a pair of stylized bronze eagles each clutching the top of its own column of polished black stone. The floor was surfaced with white marble. There were only very narrow Velcro grip-strips between the individual stones. Even if the marble was only paper-thin, it must have cost a fortune to bring it up the gravity well.

Marlowe's first impression of Raxalt was Captain Nemo. As he stood behind the huge desk, against a backdrop of the slowly turning universe, his dramatic intent was all too clear. He was a tall, slender figure in a plain, dark nehru suit without insignia or decorations. Thick gray hair was swept from a deliberately noble brow. The nose was prominent, almost predatory, and the eyes were deep-set. At the entrance of Marlowe and his escort, Raxalt looked up from the screens with a detachment that was at odds with the firm, deep voice.

"So you're Marlowe."

The escort halted with a click of heels. Marlowe simply stopped. Christine and Carmila were already standing in front of the other end of the desk, both dressed in humiliating paper coveralls. Carmila looked as bad as Marlowe guessed he did. She was sunken-eyed and forlorn without her vampire costume. She had clearly been through probe and interrogation. Christine looked comparatively healthy. The fact that she was still there proved that Murphy hadn't been let loose in her brain. Raxalt motioned to the police escort that stood with discreet menace behind the two women.

"Bring a chair for Ms. Stavers."

Marlowe noted that no chair was being offered either to him or to Carmila. One of the installation cops positioned a chair in front of the desk. It was high-backed and formal with the RAMco logo stamped in gold onto its gray leather upholstery. Christine sat down as though it was no more than her fair due. Raxalt remained standing and addressed her directly.

"It would seem that we have a standoff."

Christine nodded. She appeared to be tired. "You could call it that. I could think of other descriptions."

"We do, however, have one advantage."

"You have me."

"Exactly."

"So I'm to remain your prisoner."

"Think of yourself as a guest. A very valued guest."

"How long do you imagine that you can keep me here?"

"Almost indefinitely."

"You don't think that my people will try to get me out?"

"They might try, but I very much doubt that your corporation could mount an effective rescue operation against this installation. The single fact that you have no independent space vehicles of your own would seem to preclude such an action."

"I'm sure that one of your rivals would be more than happy to lease us whatever we might need."

"I very much doubt that. You're in space now, Ms. Stavers, and out here we don't condone actions that might endanger a facility, even a facility that is owned by another corporation. You might say that we've transcended your planetside competition. The void is a common enemy."

Christine didn't look impressed. "What is this? The brotherhood of the sea?"

"Something that goes much deeper. The empty universe is a much crueler mistress than the sea. That's what we all have in common here on the highside."

The light of fanaticism was even brighter in Raxalt's eyes than it had been in De Kuyper's. Marlowe started to wonder if all these spacemen were crazy. Christine shifted in her chair. She knew that she was losing.

"Stavers Industries could simply withdraw its services from this installation."

"Your brother and sister are not going to permit that to happen."

"They wouldn't have any choice if I ordered it."

Raxalt smiled. "But you're not going to order it. You're going to be incommunicado until we reach some sort of compromise."

He waited while that sank in. Christine didn't say anything. She didn't bother with any further squirming.

"I'm not going to give in to you," she said finally.

"Ultimately you will."

"You're very confident, Director Raxalt."

"I have to be, Ms. Stavers."

"So you might as well lock me away."

"There is one remaining problem."

"What's that?"

"These two." He indicated Marlowe and Carmila. "We have no intention of allowing these people to take up residence in this installation. They couldn't pass the most basic of selection tests. They're leisure-outs." He said the phrase in a tone of total contempt.

"So we can go home?" Marlowe asked.

Raxalt stared coldly at him. "I'm afraid not. We also can't have you running around loose on Earth. You'd undoubtedly talk to anyone who'd listen and cause as much disruption as they could."

Christine looked at Carmila and then at Raxalt. "So what are you going to do with them?"

"They'll have to be terminated."

Marlowe couldn't contain himself. "What are you talking about?"

Raxalt ignored him. One of Marlowe's escorts put a steadying hand on his shoulder.

Christine was shaking her head. "You can't do that."

Thank god, Marlowe thought. Christine was coming to the rescue. Raxalt, however, was smiling.

"My dear Ms. Stavers, I can execute anyone I want."

Christine pointed to Carmila. "This woman is my companion and personal assistant. If I'm going to be incarcerated in this place, I need her with me."

"Can she type?"

"I need her with me, Director Raxalt."

Raxalt briefly considered the idea. "Very well, you can have her. We want you to be comfortable while you're here. What about Marlowe?"

Damn right, what about Marlowe?

"I have no further use for Marlowe."

You bitch! You miserable, vicious, self-obsessed bitch!

"Then Marlowe will be immediately terminated by explosive decompression."

Marlowe took a step forward. "Wait just a goddamn minute!"

Raxalt signaled to the escort. "Restrain him."

"You can't do this to me!"

The guards grabbed him. Marlowe struggled, but they held him fast. All he could do was scream.

"You can't kill me! I haven't done anything!"

Raxalt ignored his violent protests. "Take him out and apply the standard procedure."

Marlowe was dragged bodily from the director's office, kicking, screaming, and cursing.

"You bastards can't do this to me! You can't just kill me for nothing!"

Raxalt had the escort pause. He regarded Marlowe with cold disdain. "I can do anything I want with you, you miserable little dirtsider. You're dying because you're a parasite and of utterly no use to anybody. You should reflect on that in your remaining moments. You are all of what is wrong with your planet."

Outside in the anteroom, more Installation Police were waiting. Two of them carried something that looked horribly like a bodybag. It was made from heavyweight blue plastic and networked with inflatable tubes. Marlowe was in a hyperventilating shock. This couldn't be happening! This couldn't be happening!

"What does the old man want done with this one?"

"Lock pop."

"At least that's tidy. Let's get him into the bag."

The bodybag was opened flat, and Marlowe was picked up and laid on top of it. It was pulled around him, and a thick, heavy-duty zipper was secured. The tubes were connected and a small air bottle was snapped onto a valve. The tubes began to inflate. As they expanded, Marlowe found that he was completely unable to move. It was a pneumatic straitjacket. He lay trussed on the floor while his captors discussed logistics.

"There's two others to be popped on this watch, right?"

"Couple of subversives."

"So why not do the three of them in one blowout?"

"It'd be the sensible thing to do. I'll call the holding tank. They can bring them and meet us at the lock."

"XL14?"

"That's about the same distance for each of us, and if we blow them from there, there won't be no bodies floating past the old man's window."

The bodybag came equipped with carrying handles. Marlowe was unceremoniously lifted by four officers and hauled away like so much luggage. As far as he could tell, he was being taken down towards the hub of the rotating section. Not that Marlowe particularly cared where he was being taken. All he hoped was that he would never get there. He was exploring added depths of terror. There had been some kind of intervention. He had made this last walk a thousand times in the movies. James Cagney in *Angels with Dirty Faces*, Susan Hayward in *I Want to Live*. He had always prayed that he would never have to deal with any living reality.

"It has to be some kind of mistake. You can't do this."

"Shut up or we'll gag you."

That seemed to say it all. Dignity in going to one's death was something that had been left in the twentieth century, or maybe it had only ever existed on the screen. Marlowe wasn't sure that if they had let him walk, he would have been able to. He wanted to vomit.

He wanted to vomit even more badly when they moved out of the rotating section and into the free-fall area. He wasn't aware that it was happening until the last moment. Marlowe was too busy screaming inside his own head to notice that the officers carrying him had entered the transition tube and were stepping from floor strip to floor strip, or that each moving strip was moving less slowly than the last. The first he knew was when there was a sensation of floating, and then he plunged. He started screaming with no intention of stopping. His escort didn't hesitate. A simple ball gag was stuffed into his mouth.

"Mnnf!"

"We warned you."

The plunge diminished. The rest of his senses were trying to convince his inner ear that he wasn't really falling. The neural debate was far from comfortable. In free-fall, Marlowe wasn't even being carried—he was floating. One cop was towing him on a nylon leash attached to the neck seal of the body bag, while the others walked beside. He had been reduced to mere mass, and very soon that mass would be exploded all over the immediate universe. This couldn't be happening. He had lived most of his life in fantasy—was it possible that he was going to die in extreme reality? Was it going to hurt? Dear god, he was accepting the situation.

"Here we are, dirtside. External Airlock 14. This is the end of your road. One with the infinite from now on."

Another of the squad was looking around impatiently. "Where are those assholes from the holding tank?"

There was the hiss of an opening bulkhead.

"Here they are."

"Let's get this over with."

Marlowe was pointed in the wrong direction to see anything of the other victims. What did one have to do up here to be designated a subversive? If his example was anything to go by, it probably wasn't very much.

One of his guards was rubbing the small inspection window of the inner airlock door with his sleeve. "Damn thing seems to be iced up on the inside. I can't see a thing in there."

"Maybe it's on the fritz."

One of the squad from the holding tank was operating the lock controls. "Everything showing normal on the board."

"If it's breached, it won't open anyway."

"Ready them up, it's starting to open."

A number of guards put restraining hands on Marlowe, taking precautions against a final spasm of desperate violence. They needn't have bothered. Marlowe was paralyzed. The lock was opening. It was dark inside. Something was moving in there. Three figures were coming fast out of the lock. Two wore red spacesuits; the other wore dark green. They were heavy-duty work suits with plates of plastic exo-armor covering the more vulnerable parts of the body, making their wearers resemble something out of a samurai nightmare. The visors were dark and anonymous. There were weapons in their gloved fists—not swords, however, but triple-barreled, large-bore handguns. There were repeated explosions. The spacesuit figures swayed as they fired, even with what had to be minimized recoil. Marlowe's escort went spinning backward in a tangle of arms and legs, sailing back down the corridor that led away from the lock until they crashed into a wall or a bulkhead. The figures kept on firing until there wasn't an officer standing. One of the other prisoners had started drifting away. The figure in green grabbed for the leash.

"Everybody relax. We're getting you out of here."

The distorted voice was coming from a helmet speaker. Another voice cut in.

"Get the bags on them and let's get out of here."

Something was being pulled over Marlowe's head. It did resemble a plastic bag, but in fact it was a soft emergency space helmet. A small oxygen pack was slapped on his chest and one of the figures in red was dragging him into the airlock. The six of them waited in the chamber, the three figures in suits and the three trussed prisoners. As the lock exhausted, the soft helmet ballooned away from Marlowe's face. Warning lights flashed and the outer door silently opened. One of the red spacesuits had hold of Marlowe's leash and moved fast, straight through the door. Marlowe found that he was being dragged straight out of lock and into empty space. Fear went into overload and he took the easy way out. He fainted.

NINE

SOMEONE WAS SLAPPING AND SHAKING HIM.

"Wake up, boyo. This won't do. You can't sleep here."

Marlowe opened his eyes to see a leathery face with bushy eyebrows and bright blue eyes staring into his.

"That's better. Come on. See if you can stand."

Firm hands were guiding his feet toward a Velcro strip on what might have been the floor but could just as easily have been the wall. He had been removed from the body-bag. He was still wearing the paper suit, but someone had slipped a pair of Velcro slippers on him. The slippers made contact with the strip. He was anchored. It wasn't like gravity, but it did give him a partial sense of up and down. He stood, swaying slightly like a reed in the wind or maybe one of those kids' inflatable punching bags that always regain their equilibrium.

"Where am I?"

"Will you listen to him? What did you have to rescue a goddamn dirtsider for?"

Someone grunted.

"He was being popped along with Toshiro and Alf. What were we supposed to do? Leave him behind?"

"Might have been the best thing. We don't even know who he is."

"So who is he?"

The man with the bushy eyebrows had taken a step back. Behind him a second man was peeling off a red spacesuit.

"Who are you?"

"I'm Marlowe."

"He's Marlowe."

"What is that supposed to mean?"

They seemed to be inside an irregular, podlike bubble of soft, opaque plastic, a misshapen section of tubing maybe four meters across and twelve from end to end. Large, crude murals were painted on the inside of the plastic, some wholly abstract, others realistically obscene. Clothing and personal possessions were secured to the walls by webbing nets that appeared to be the free-fall equivalent of shelving. Also attached to the wall were objects not unlike the bodybag in which he had almost gone to his death. Marlowe assumed that they had to be zero-gravity bunks of some kind. At each end of the tubular section, there was a simple flap door system, designed to seal automatically in the event of a pressure loss.

"Why don't you try to walk? The rule is always to keep one foot on the ground."

It was easier said than done. Marlowe took an exploratory step and lost the Velcro; the two men had to grab him before he drifted to the subjective ceiling.

"It's all in the feet, boyo. It's all in the feet. Reach for the strip each time you move."

"You better get the hang of walking pretty damn fast, Marlowe, or whatever your name is, because pretty soon this pipe is going to be crawling with gestapo."

The other man was now out of the red spacesuit and was attaching it to a set of wall-mounted clips. He was younger than the one with bushy eyebrows. Both of them watched as Marlowe experimented with free-fall walking. Finally he managed three consecutive steps and paused for breath.

"What are the gestapo?"

"The IPs, the Installation Police."

"The jokers you were just rescued from."

The man who had just taken off the red suit was a hard, capable type with close-cropped dark hair. His face was closed and swarthy, and he wore a religious medallion around his neck. Although he had no noticeable accent, Marlowe suspected that he was from somewhere in the Middle East. He was certain that the man didn't trust him.

"Can you walk?"

Marlowe tried a couple more steps. "Just about."

"Then let's get going."

The man with the cropped hair indicated that Marlowe should go first. Marlowe did as he was told. He pushed his way through the flap door and found that he was in another podlike chamber, although this one appeared to be unoccupied. They crossed the chamber and went through the far flap, made their way through two more connected chambers, and then came to a second flap covering a manhole in what Marlowe had come to think of as the floor. His companion indicated that he should open the flap and drop down into the hole.

"We'll be able to move faster in the conduit."

"The conduit?"

The manhole led to a tunnel that housed the plumbing and power lines that served the plastic pods. Handholds were set in the wall of the tunnel, so the men could float free, hauling themselves along by their arms. It was a good deal speedier than the clumsy, Velcro-anchored walking. As far as Marlowe could figure it, these pods, and the tunnel that serviced them, had to be a part of the long streamers of placbag tubing that he had seen from De Kuyper's office.

He glanced back at the man with the close-cropped hair. "Where are we going?"

"What does it matter? You don't know where you are."

"We're in the placbag tubes, right?"

"What do you know about the tubes?" There was suspicion in the man's voice.

"Almost nothing. I saw them just once from De Kuyper's office."

"You were in De Kuyper's office?"

Marlowe was quick to explain. "I was taken there before they probed me."

The man grunted. For the moment, at least, he seemed

satisfied. They went on hauling themselves down the conduit.

"There's an exit flap coming up. Pull yourself up through it and don't try anything. I'll be right behind you."

The exit flap led into yet another empty pod. Marlowe floated himself through the manhole and reached for the Velcro floor strips with his slippered foot. He waited for cropped hair to emerge. When they were both on their feet, the man pointed to the flap at the other end.

"Through there."

The next pod was twice the size of all the previous pods that Marlowe had passed through, and it was far from empty. His first impression was of a strange combination of boudoir and high-tech junkyard. Festoons of electrical cables snaked through the area like vines in a jungle. Video monitors, touch decks, and banks of electronic equipment that Marlowe couldn't even identify were stacked in makeshift, erector-set racks. The crudity of their arrangement seemed to indicate that whoever used them leaned toward the organic rather than the precise. The effect of serpentine chaos was heightened by the fact that the double-size pod was hot, dark, and humid. A humidifier on the ceiling pumped out a constant miniature gusher of water vapor. The boudoir started with the thick smell of perfume on the air and the silk streamers that were tied at random to power cables and rack frames and floated sinuously on the circulating air. A field of a luxurious mutant moss, which resembled long golden-green fur, was spreading down one section of the wall.

In the middle of this confusion, all but englobed by hardware, was a young woman dressed in white bikini briefs and a cut-down T-shirt. She was loosely strapped into a double-sized contour berth and surrounded by tethered cushions. She was playing with the electronics using a miniaturized but highly elaborate Conpro masterdeck balanced on her lap. She was slim and athletic, probably Scandinavian, and, counter to the normal off-world taste for little hair or none, she wore hers long. On Earth, her straight blond locks would have hung well past her waist, but in free-fall they haloed her head like an exotic puffball, rippling and swaying like something underwater each time she moved, and glistening in the light of the monitors that surrounded her.

She looked up as Marlowe pushed his way through the flap. "Don't you knock?"

"I'm sorry. I . . ."

"I don't know you, do I?"

"No . . ."

By this time, cropped hair had pushed his way through the lock.

"Aman! Is everything okay?" She had put aside the masterdeck and was unstrapping herself from the contour berth. She looked concerned. "Did everything go okay?"

"We got Alf and Toshiro out okay, but there was one factor we hadn't planned for."

"What was that?"

Aman pointed to Marlowe. "Him."

The woman ducked her head as she floated dexterously between the racks of equipment. With the grace of a ballet dancer, she extended a foot for a Velcro anchor.

"What is he?" she asked.

"That's the problem. We don't know. He was being popped along with the other two."

"So you brought him here?"

"We had to move fast. The gestapo are going to be all over the barrack tubes any minute. They never bother you here."

"There's always a first time. I don't mind skating for you, but I'm hardly equipped to harbor fugitives."

Aman looked uncomfortable. "Come on, Ices. What were we supposed to do? We had no time to set anything up."

Ices? The woman's name was Ices?

"You know anything about him at all?"

"He's a dirtsider and he says his name's Marlowe."

"And he was about to be executed?"

"That's how it seemed."

"I'll get in and see what I can find. If he was scheduled for lock pop, he ought to ref in the IP's general roster."

She swung back to the contour berth, snapped the strap across her waist, and picked up the deck.

"Let's slide into IP shallows and see where the flow takes us." She glanced up at Marlowe. "I'm Ices, by the way."

"Ices."

"That's what they call me."

"I'm pleased to meet you."

"Let's hope so." She talked as she worked. "I built all this stuff myself. It may look like shit, but there are very few data blocks on this station that I can't access with it. I'm the best systems writer they've got, so they have to tolerate my life-style. Most of the time they don't know what I'm doing. Hold it . . . here we go."

Her finger flew over the touches as characters rolled across three of the monitors.

"Good god."

"What?" Aman asked.

"According to his file, he came up here with the Stavers woman."

"He's one of hers?"

"Apparently not. Get this. He's a leisure-out from the Zone and he's only here because of some monumental screwup back planetside."

Marlowe sighed. "That's what I've been trying to tell everyone ever since I got here."

Both Ices and Aman ignored him.

"Let's run the probe results," she said.

Her fingers danced again. She watched the screens as the columns of characters changed to a scrolling montage of characters and images. Every so often she nodded to herself. Finally the run stopped and she let her hands fall from the deck.

"It seems to check. Of course, he still could be a gestapo plant, but that would involve the other side knowing one hell of a lot more about our doings than they ought to. In theory, they might have probed the real Marlowe and disposed of him and this isn't him at all. It seems a lot of trouble to go to unless they were fairly sure that there was someone like me skating their data. It was also one hell of a risk, even with a fully expendable plant, to stake everything on the fact that we'd stage a rescue of Alf and Toshiro. It's too subtle for De Kuyper's thinking. It's not his style at all."

Aman frowned. "Raxalt could think up something like that."

Ices smiled. "You know something? I've been vectoring Raxalt. I'm not sure that he really thinks the way you and I might define it."

"What does he do?"

"He probably has visions or some shit like that. I'm starting to think that he's some kind of throwback to the biblical prophets. There's no logic to anything he does. Just this continuing vision. It's weird. According to any reasonable criteria, he shouldn't exist, let alone be let loose in space. Weirdest of all is that it works after a fashion."

"This still doesn't answer the question of what we do with Marlowe."

Ices shook her head. Her hair undulated. "I think we have to accept him on face value. The odds are in his favor."

"So we accept him. What then?"

"I figure we have two options. We either fake him an identity and take him in as one of us, or we pitch him out of a lock and forget we ever saw him."

Marlowe lost his temper. "Would someone care to listen to me for a change? So far, I've been shot at, kidnapped, dragged into space, tortured, and almost executed. Now you're talking about killing me again. Why is it that everyone wants to dump me out of an airlock? Don't I have say in any of this?"

Ices's face wasn't without sympathy. "It's just so tidy to dump you. It closes the file. There are no loose ends."

Where had he heard that before? "Tidy? My life's worth more than tidy, goddamn it!"

Ices glanced at Aman. "It'd probably be our best bet to keep him around."

Aman didn't look happy. "How do you figure that?"

"We still don't know exactly what Raxalt has in mind for Stavers. We do know that he hasn't probed her, so there must be some sort of negotiation going on."

Marlowe interruped. "It's a standoff, as a matter of fact."

Ices beamed. "There you go. He may actually be able

to help us. I think we should keep him around for the moment.''

Aman wasn't convinced. ''How the hell do we bury him? He can hardly walk weightless. He screams dirt-sider with every move.''

Ices didn't seem particularly bothered. ''I'll think of something. If all else fails we'll stash him in the sick bay. Claim his legs are broken. I tell you what, why don't you get yourself to wherever you're supposed to be and leave him here with me? He's going to need some clothes, and I'll make a start on creating an identity for him. I'll bring him to the Golden Slipper around shift change and we can take it from there.''

Aman looked shocked. ''Are you out of your mind? You want to take him to a bar?''

''The old maxim about hiding out in a crowd was pretty much on the money.''

''But I already told you that he can't walk worth a damn.''

''And the Golden Slipper's on a spinner, Aman my love. I imagine he can walk perfectly well in gravity.''

Aman still wasn't happy. ''I hope you know what you're doing.''

''Have some faith, baby.''

Aman shrugged resignedly and then shot a final warning look at Marlowe. ''I'll be watching you. You'd better not turn out to be a plant.''

After he'd left, Ices turned her attention to Marlowe. He had brightened considerably. He wasn't going to be fired out of an airlock, and there might even be a drink in his future.

''I've got to thank you for talking your pal Aman out of wasting me.''

''Like I said, the odds were on your side, and besides, you've got an honest face.'' She looked him up and down. ''You are a sorry sight, though. The paper suit really doesn't do it. I think the first thing is to get you some decent clothes. Dressed properly, you wouldn't look quite so gulag. You want a drink?''

''Now?''

Marlowe was amazed. For some inexplicable reason

he had never visualized people in space keeping booze around. Ices was again unstrapping herself.

"Why not? You look like you could use one." She floated in the direction of a small fridge that was mounted on a solid section of outer wall. "It's only the local gin, I'm afraid. It's cold, though."

"Right now, I'd drink antifreeze."

"We can do slightly better than that. You know how to use a squeeze bottle?"

"I think so."

"You just put your lips together and suck."

The local gin was pretty appalling, but Marlowe was more than grateful. He was even starting to like free-fall—it could be quite relaxing if one let oneself go with it.

"How did you get the name Ices?" he asked.

"My second name is Berg."

She picked up a small universal scanner. "I should take your measurements." She pointed it at him. "You were a leisure-out, right?"

"That's right."

"Were you a period piece?"

"I was a forty."

"Hence Marlowe. I get it. What did you do? Some variation on Humphrey Bogart?"

"Something like that."

"You won't get no threads like that up here."

"Could I get away with John Garfield in a trucker movie?"

Ices laughed. "I'll see what I can do."

Marlowe realized that it had been a long time since he had heard anyone laugh.

Ices picked up a phone, which Marlowe noted was audio only. "Yo. Huey. I need some used clothes. I'm sending the specs down now. Garbage them after you've filled the order. . . . Great, I love you, too." She hung up. "While we're waiting for the clothes, I'll see if I can build you an identity."

Once again her fingers moved over the Conpro. She was apparently able to work and talk at the same time. "How are things planetside?"

Marlowe sucked on the squeeze bottle. "Things keep

getting worse. Everybody secretly knows it's screwed. I'm surprised that you asked. Nobody up here seems very interested in what's going on down on Earth."

"We're a pretty elitist bunch. I'd be as bad as anyone else except I like to keep up with events."

"Do you ever go back?"

"Not anymore."

For the next two hours, Ices gave Marlowe a fairly comprehensive rundown on the pressures and politics of outer space. It turned out that it was quite as much of a mess of powerplay and intrigue as anything that he had encountered back on the planet. Raxalt, effectively out of reach of even the RAMco board and backed by De Kuyper's police, had just about succeeded in turning the installation into a virtual dictatorship. On Earth, there was a general cozy assumption, possibly even shared by high-ranking corporate executives, that the expansion into space was simply an extension of business as usual. A certain heavy-handedness was expected on the part of those in charge on the front line. That was the pioneer way. As far as the dirtsiders were concerned, space enjoyed the same kind of hands-off, lack of direct control that had been enjoyed by the people who, a half century earlier, had torn into the Amazon claiming they were finally opening it up to the twenty-first century. Ultimately they had destroyed it, but that was something that just wasn't talked about. As long as the precision goods and the microbeams came back from space, the same sort of benign neglect applied. What Marlowe was rapidly learning was that this orbiting environment was nothing like the Amazon development. That had always remained firmly tied to the corporate interests in Brasilia, Miami, and Zurich. Even though the booming space stations still relied on manpower, raw materials, consumer goods, and even food and water that had to be brought up the gravity well the hard way, emotional and psychological apron strings were being severed. Those who had made a home in space quite literally looked down at the planet that had given them birth. They saw themselves as superior beings creating a superior world.

"It's not just Raxalt's and De Kuyper's overt fascism. In many respects, that's already old-fashioned and in time it'll die out. Even among the rank and file, there's what you could call a definite highside chauvinism. It's probably an Oedipal thing. They came here because they couldn't fuck Mother Earth and now they despise everything of and about her. You may well have trouble with this. Even the base-rate welder thinks dirtsiders are a slug's second cousin."

"Are you telling me that empires are founded on self-hate?"

"Aren't they? Ask the Incas. A man at peace with himself doesn't need to go traipsing around in the unknown, slaughtering anything that gets in his way."

Despite Ices's confidence that Raxalt and his vision would eventually become a thing of the past, there were plenty on the installation who were far from willing to wait for its natural demise. A healthy and extensive, if rather anarchic, underground flourished, defying all of De Kuyper's efforts to stamp out subversion. The underground was a far from cohesive alliance of a host of divergent groups that stretched from protolabor unions at one end of the spectrum to drugged-out rocket trash at the other. Only an autocrat like Raxalt could focus their resentment and stop them from coming apart at the seams. The one advantage that the rank-and-file underground had over Raxalt and his gestapo was that they had put the space station together and, between them, they knew every centimeter of the huge structure. Subversion had been physically built into the very fabric of the environment. Hiding places and clandestine float tubes and corridors had been created simply by ignoring the plans. The vast computer system was penetrated and compromised at every junctionbox and laser reflector. Ices's lair was one of the major patchpoints for the two-way flow of information.

"The joy of it is that I can not only steal their secrets but also feed in any nonsense that I think will confuse them."

The underground wasn't without its own blunt effectiveness. If nothing else, it kept the police on their toes. There were large areas, particularly the workers' barrack tubes and some of the construction sites, into which the police couldn't go except in full-scale raiding force. The only place where they enjoyed a sense of absolute control was the rotating administration wheel. The conflict between the authorities and the rebels was basically a chess game of thrust and counterthrust. There would be an assassination, maybe one of Raxalt's junior aides or a cop making himself a reputation for brutality. De Kuyper would then hit back with arrests and executions. A locker room of police spacesuits would be sabotaged, and a few days later a tactical squad of the gestapo would storm into the barrack tubes, busting stills, confiscating drug stashes, and making summary arrests. It was a circular dance in which neither side could gain the upper hand—Raxalt and his police were too well entrenched, and the opposition was too able to blend into the regular workforce.

"It's like Chairman Mao said; 'The revolutionary moves like a fish through water.' "

"Aren't you afraid that eventually some nut will blow up the entire fishtank?"

Ices shook her head. "Neither side wants to destroy the environment. This is our own world. If it's destroyed, we would have to go back to Earth. Nobody wants that. We all have some sort of vision. We want to be in space as badly as Raxalt. It's just that we want things run differently. I mean, check out the weapons that are being used. None of them can do serious damage to the fabric of the station. We're not ripping the place apart with retuned lasers. We've learned better than that. It's a war of rubber bullets and bird shot and stun guns, even knives and razors. A razor cut in a spacesuit can be quite as deadly as a bullet. We're not going to trash this place the way the planet was trashed."

Aside from the glimpses of her own definite sense of superiority over those who remained back on Earth, Marlowe felt comfortable around Ices. She had a cool, assured intelligence that was tempered by hints of a wild, blond, iconoclastic passion. He hoped he would find a way to know her better. What was really refreshing was that she didn't exhibit the cultivated psychoses that were such a part of most of the women that he had met recently. Getting to know her better might not be too easy.

Romance was a bitch when one was living one hour at a time.

After about forty minutes, the clothes arrived. Marlowe looked around for some cubbyhole where he could change in private. There wasn't one. Ices caught his glance.

"Don't mind me. Go straight ahead. Privacy is at a premium around here. I'm very lucky to have this place to myself."

Marlowe turned his back and unfastened the snaps on the paper suit. He was getting a little tired of stripping in front of strangers.

"You've got a nice ass, Marlowe."

"Thanks."

The well-worn khaki jumpsuit was decorated with patches from a ship called the *Triton.*

"What happened to the *Triton*?" Marlowe asked.

"She was broken up years ago."

"Am I likely to meet anyone who served on her?"

"It's unlikely. I checked. The *Triton* was only a class-one shuttle. You could have merely ridden on her as a passenger and picked up the patches as souvenirs. There's also a constant trade in patches and decals, so I wouldn't worry about it too much."

Dressing in free-fall proved to be something of a challenge. Marlowe got one leg into the jumpsuit, but then he pivoted awkwardly, lost his grip on the Velcro, and found himself windmilling in midair.

Ices was very patient. "Grab something solid and push off with your arms. Then find an anchor as you float. You've got to get used to this."

Marlowe found his feet on the third try. "This is ridiculous."

He managed to get into the jumpsuit without any further mishap, then inspected the World War II—style, fur-collared, leather bomber jacket.

"Isn't this a little warm for around here?"

"Believe me, Marlowe, the heat in this place is far from uniform. That jacket may save your life one day."

The ensemble was completed by a pair of black Velcro-soled Keds Skywalkers and a navy-blue, duck-billed cap. Marlowe wasn't sure about the cap. With the jacket and jumpsuit, he might not have been John Garfield, but he felt it gave him a certain roustabout style that looked okay for outer space. The cap, on the other hand, turned him into Arnold Stang.

"Do I have to wear this?"

Ices nodded. "Wear it, trust me. It'll hide your face. There's one other thing. You really ought to get a haircut before too long. There's only a few of us, me—and the rastas, of course—that let their hair grow long. You can't afford to stand out."

"So where do I get a haircut?"

"There're a bunch of barber shops in the tubes. You'll find they have a definite social function, particularly among the construction workers. If you get drunk enough, you can get a tattoo at the same time." Ices herself, he noticed, had a small blue and purple butterfly tattooed on her thigh.

Marlowe's fake identity was that of an anonymous roustabout called Jimmy Dean Garvin who had ripped his spacesuit on a projecting girder and gone into explosive decompression. Ices had garbaged the death record and supered on Marlowe's face, fingerprints, retinals, and all other distinguishing features. Finally she ran out hard copy: ID plate, backup papers, and even a credit cone.

"You'll actually be drawing pay."

"Let's hope I live to spend it."

"I figure you'll make it. You're harder than you pretend."

A small amber light was flashing on Ices's master deck. She beckoned to Marlowe. "Watch this, it should amuse you."

She hit a couple of touches and the same image appeared on three screens. Marlowe's jaw dropped.

"I don't believe it."

"Believe it."

"But . . . De Kuyper? What is this? A simulation?"

"It's the real thing. I've had a vid tap into the chief's private sex bunker for some weeks now."

The supervisor of police was provocatively clad in black leather trunks with a studded codpiece hanging from the crotch. He was vigorously caning a naked figure who squirmed against the straps that held it down to an inverted contour berth. The figure was very slim, and with its all but shaved head, Marlowe had trouble distinguishing the sex.

"Is that a boy or a girl?"

"Girl, actually, although it's not always. This one's a DI2 in Admin Intelligence."

"This doesn't seem a particularly intelligent thing to do."

"For her point of view, it's probably a shrewd career move. I've come across her before. She's an ambitious little bitch, and singularly determined."

"Maybe she's enjoying herself."

"Maybe. If she is, she's on to a definite plus, but I think it's more likely that she's gritting her teeth and thinking of promotion."

"Does he do this a lot?"

"Oh, sure. He's very big on the old-world decadence and he doesn't hesitate to use his position to get who or what he wants."

"How in hell did you get a camera in there?"

"I didn't have to. There're goddamn cameras everywhere on the admin wheel. When De Kuyper commissioned his little love nest, he didn't remove the camera. That would have left a hole in the big-brother net. Instead, he gimmicked it so it always showed a simulation of a harmless storage bay, which is what the place was to begin with. I just degimmicked the setup so it fed the real deal into my system. One day I'll simulcast it on all the general entertainment channels at once. I'm just waiting for the right moment."

Marlowe was staring at the screens. "That's got to hurt."

A beeping came from somewhere inside the equipment and a number of lights started flashing. Marlowe looked around in alarm.

"What's that?"

"That's the shift change. We have to start moving."

Ices propelled herself across the room, dropped the door of a closet, and pulled something out. With expertise that put Marlowe to shame, she seemed to glide into a black bodysuit. She slung a pair of gold high heels over one shoulder, reminding Marlowe of a skater en route to the rink.

"We're going to gravity so I can wear heels."

"I thought we weren't supposed to stand out."

"You're not. I have a reputation to keep up." She took one last look at herself in a mirror. "Get your coat and hat, Marlowe. We're going to the Golden Slipper."

Marlowe grabbed the leather jacket and cap from where he had parked them in midair. Ices paused before dropping through the flap door.

"Remember this is the new frontier."

"What's that supposed to mean?"

"So far, you've only seen the genteel side of this place."

They went back into the conduit for the first leg of the trip to the bar. Marlowe found that he had gotten the hang of this simple, hand-over-hand, forward motion and could easily keep up with Ices. As they floated down the narrow tube, Ices explained how her capsule was at the far end of a largely unused tube that was moored to the only partially constructed center section.

"It's the solitude of the deep thinker," she added.

The next stage of the journey wasn't quite so simple.

"From here we take a bus."

Marlowe looked at her as though she were crazy. "A what?"

"A bus. The standard close-range shuttle. A flat tin can full of grab bars with a chemical burner on its underside. It's the local mass transit that gets us proles from one end of the environment to the other. They putter along hanging close to the surface."

"You mean we're going out into space? Don't we need suits?"

"Not on the buses. They nose-seal up to a lock and you just walk on. Of course, if they get hit by a chunk of debris, they burst like a balloon. It doesn't happen too often, though, so you pretty much play the odds."

Marlowe tried to ignore these last unwelcome tidbits. "There seems to be a good deal of odds-playing up here."

"That's what pioneering's all about."

They emerged from the conduit into an open area in

front of a large airlock. Although it was pressurized, there was heavy-duty, interior construction going on and the air was filled with a cacophony of yells and hammering, the stammer of rivet guns, and the hum and crackle of welding lasers. Marlowe ducked as a large steel machine riding on air thrusters, the weightless equivalent of a forklift, pushed a thick stack of prefabricated room sections low over his head.

"You got to watch your ass around here," Ices said.

Marlowe experienced a momentary gut wrench as he lost his footing while Velcro-walking toward the airlock. Fortunately there was something of a crowd, all moving in the same direction, and nobody noticed.

Ices hissed at him. "Don't get ambitious. Just shuffle."

They waited ten minutes before the bus arrived, and the warning lights around the lock started flashing and sirens shrilled. The lock rotated open and the crowd moved forward. Marlowe was surprised to discover that they were entering the saucer-shaped transport through the top. What was subjectively the far wall was covered in red Velcro. As the travelers passed through the lock, they flipped their bodies through ninety degrees, feet forward, and then moved hand over hand along the interlocking soft plastic grab bars until their feet were anchored on the red floor. Ices surreptitiously grabbed a handful of the back of Marlowe's jumpsuit and flipped him to the right attitude as she made her own move, then guided him down to anchorage.

"You'll get it. You're really learning quite fast."

A voice came from the bus's PA. "Everybody red-floored? We're moving out."

Marlowe felt his boots trying to tug away from the floor as the craft retroed away from the lock. When the main engine cut in, though, right under his feet, he was treated to a mild sensation of weight. That was nothing, however, compared to what hit him when the bus, after four stops, matched velocity with the rotating section that was their destination. The PA had made a single curt announcement.

"Weight coming up, folks. Get ready."

He felt like an enormous hand was pushing him into the

floor. His legs buckled. The only consolation was that he wasn't alone—a number of other people seemed to be suffering similar strain. It took him a full minute or more to get his legs back and step into the cage elevator that was their means of exit at this end of the trip. This prompted another brief lecture from Ices as they made the lengthy but increasingly normal walk to the level on which the Golden Slipper was situated.

"The gyms are all in rotating areas, except the free-fall dance space. You really have to work out at least three times a week and calcium-pack all the time."

Marlowe had laughed. "Me? Work out?"

"If you don't want your bones to snap when you walk back into gravity."

Marlowe didn't laugh anymore. While the idea sank in, Ices stooped down and snapped the straps of her gold high heels.

Nothing in his short experience of space had prepared Marlowe for the Golden Slipper. He had been half expecting something sterile, brightly lit, and joylessly institutional. He had been imagining something along the lines of the techdoom joints in the Zone where livingdead figures, shaking with induced paranoia, circled in blueglare and monotonous metanoise, too afraid to meet each other's eyes, let alone talk. He was pleasantly surprised to find that the space tavern was dirty, dark, and roaring. Ices's remark about the new frontier started to make sense. This was a saloon in the time-honored tradition.

They pushed open the batwing doors and stepped inside. The ceiling was low and the air was smoky. Tobacco, ganja, and perfume blended with a sweetly metallic chemical smell that Marlowe had never encountered before. The roar of boisterous, shouted conversation was augmented by the sound of James Brown with the famous Flames backtrack juiced almost beyond recognition. Marlowe realized that the men and women of the space station were engaged in hard and dangerous work—and demanded the right to play equally hard.

The bar itself was a large circular affair on top of which a pair of near naked go-boys danced and pranced. The bar top was made of sheets of white translucent plastic that were lit from below and gave those immediately around it a sinister aquarium look. A female stripper was writhing and twisting on a small stage of her own. The crew was a motley one. The majority were in slightly more go-to-party versions of their regular work clothes. There was an abundance of jumpsuits, blue jeans, pressure vests, and lumberjack shirts. A minority, though, still stuck with their dirtside styles. Cowboys romped and stomped in fringes and Stetsons. Muscle men in chains, leather, and tattoos could only have been recruited from the ranks of truck jocks. At the other extreme, there was a small coterie of giggling and pouting transvestites. Marlowe noticed that there was a remarkably high proportion of dreadlocked rastas. Nobody had to tell him that it took all kinds to conquer space.

There was also a smattering of young women in provocative clothing, and even a handful of young men who didn't seem to have any qualms about exposing padded crotches and rouged nipples. Marlowe wondered if these people were simply making every moment of their downtime count, or if they were actual on-the-job professionals. He glanced up at one of the go-boys. Did RAMco actually import prostitutes and cooch dancers of both sexes? He shrugged. It made sense if it kept the workers quiet—except the workers weren't quiet. What the hell, doubtless he'd find out soon enough. A sign said there was a special on generic tequila.

Light sculptures gave the place a distinct festive drama as their changing colors were reflected in the sweating faces of the crowd. A formless fiberscope undulated with abstract, computer-generated sexuality while red and green display lasers sliced through the blue air. A hologram of Tempest Storm disintegrated and reassembled across the ceiling reminding Marlowe of *The Attack of the 50-Foot Woman.*

"Welcome to Babylon in space," Ices said.

She and Marlowe were hardly inside the place when she was grabbed by a broad, powerful, swarthy individual with a half-grown beard, a cropped-down mohawk, and big, industrial-strength cortical feeds set in his forehead. If there ever were space pirates, he would have made a more than adequate prototype. He danced Ices around him twice, then held her at arm's length and inspected her.

"Looking good, baby. Where you been?"

"Avoiding you."

"Don't say that, baby. You know I been missing you. It's been forever."

"It's hardly been a month, and even then I made it clear that it wasn't going to be any regular thing."

The prototype space pirate leaned close to her. "Listen, I got an idea. Why don't you and me go somewhere? I'm shipping out with some ice prospectors in the morning."

"Forget it, Ishmael. Go right on getting drunk. There's plenty of girls for hire. You won't know the difference."

The pirate's eyes lighted on Marlowe. "Who the hell is this?"

"Just a friend."

For an instant, Marlowe blanked out his new name. Then it came back to him and he stuck out a hand. "Jimmy Dean Garvin."

Ishmael ignored the hand and looked at Ices. "New boyfriend?"

Ices was firm. "Just a friend."

He glared at Marlowe. "I know you, don't I?"

Marlowe was about to deny that they had ever met but thought better of it. It was never too early to start confusing the trail. "It's possible. I've been around."

"Sure." Ishmael seemed at a loss. He took one last wistful look at Ices, shook his head, and lurched away.

Marlowe wiped his palms on the pants of his jumpsuit. He had started to sweat. "You've got some choice friends."

"Ishmael? He's okay. There's plenty worse than him. Deep-space navigators are all a little crazy. It's the bolts in their heads."

They pushed their way through the crowd and ordered drinks. Ices drank black russians. Beside them, a Japanese man with the insignia of a shuttle pilot was brandishing a bulky plastic cooler and shouting for the bartender. "Get this shit before it melts. Ice from the dawn of time."

Marlowe glanced at Ices. "What's this all about?"

"They like to bring back still-frozen ice straight off an asteroid. The Japanese are fascinated by the concept of cooling their drinks with something that's been out there for a couple of trillion years. It probably has something to do with being raised on Godzilla."

Marlowe, with a couple of generic tequilas under his belt, was starting to relax for the first time in he couldn't remember how long when Ices touched him warningly on the arm.

"I don't like the look of this."

Marlowe turned. Aman was coming in their direction, and he didn't have the appearance of a man who was there to join in the fun. He stopped beside them and looked around furtively.

"We've got troubles."

"What's happened?"

"They killed Philco. He was garroted. His body turned up in a corridor on L42 that's hardly ever used."

"Gestapo?"

"I think the unofficial kill crews are out again. There're also regular patrols all over."

"What's happened to Toshiro and Alf?"

"We got them out on a deep ranger. They're safe."

Ices was thoughtful. "So all we have to worry about is random reprisals."

"Isn't that bad enough?"

"Don't be a hypocrite, lover. You know as well as I do that if the kill crews go on the rampage again it'll stir up more unrest than we ever could. People don't like stumbling across the bodies of their friends and work-mates."

Marlowe, who was signaling for a drink, took another look at Ices. He hadn't realized that the hardness went that deep. "Maybe I should make myself scarce for a while."

Aman glared at him. "You stay right where you are."

Ices raised an eyebrow. "You still want to kill him?"

"If he's a plant, we're all dead."

Ices shook her head. "He's not a plant."

"We should at least get him out of here."

"It'd be stupid to move now. If it's like you say, we

don't want to risk running into a patrol. We might as well stay right here for the moment."

It was Aman's turn to shake his head. "I've got to go. There's too much to do."

"So go. He and I'll stay here and get out with the rest of the crowd."

"You'll go on looking after him?"

Ices shot Marlowe a glance that he couldn't quite read. "Sure, I'll take care of him."

Aman nodded and hurried away through the crowd. It was starting to dawn on Marlowe that Aman and his particular bunch of revolutionaries might not be very good at rebellion. The man seemed to live on the verge of panic. On the other hand there was Ices—she seemed to be good at everything.

She caught his thoughtful expression and tried to look reassuring. "Have a drink, pal. It may be a long night."

Aman's arrival had quite spoiled the mood, but Marlowe did his best to get back into it. Three more drinks had him swaying a little, but now that Aman had reminded him, they couldn't kill the feeling that he was a wanted fugitive. The drunken festivities continued to whirl around him, but he couldn't pretend that he was a part of it anymore. Small echoes of the Zone pricked him into a low-key mourning for his old, easy, leisure-out life where all he'd had to worry about were the routine street hassles. It seemed like a golden age. He forced himself to take a deep breath. Maybe he should slow down on the booze; he didn't want to top off the rest of his confusion with a bout of homesickness.

Just then Ishmael came back. Ices was a short distance away talking to three other women. Marlowe spotted him rolling his way through the crowd a few seconds before Ishmael saw him. A young woman with a hard, painted face and a shimmering optic wig was hanging on his arm. She was one of the ones that Marlowe was becoming increasingly convinced were imported bimbos. At first, it looked as though Ismael would lumber blindly by him, but then, at the last minute, their eyes met. Ishmael disengaged himself from the girl in the wig and glared balefully at Marlowe.

"So you're the one that's screwing Ices."

Marlowe shook his head. "I'm not screwing Ices."

Ishmael's eyes focused and unfocused. "Then you should be. She's one hell of a woman. I ought to know, I really loved that girl." He blinked. "Trouble was, she never loved me." He swung around and roared at Ices. "You never loved me, did you?"

Ices answered without missing a beat of her other conversation. "That's right, Ishmael. I never loved you."

Ishmael appealed to Marlowe. "See what I mean?"

The young woman in the wig was starting to show signs of impatience. She was regarding Ishmael with a tight, angry expression. "I don't have time for this drunken crap. Are you coming with me or what?"

Ishmael pushed her away. The move wasn't violent, but it was certainly final. "Piss off. There are plenty more where you came from."

She cursed him and flounced away. Ishmael turned back to Marlowe and put a confiding arm around his shoulder.

"I got to tell you, pal. You don't have to put up with this kind of shit in the deeps. Deep space, Jack. The only place that a man can find a little peace. You ever been in deep space?"

Marlowe shook his head. He was as far out as he ever wanted to get. "Not me."

"You should try it."

"Sure."

"That's what's wrong with all this orbital shit. It's too damn close to Earth. Too much of the same old waltz 'round. We should have done what the Russians done. We should have gone straight on to Mars. Talk about the red planet. One thing, though, all this bull will vanish when we finally meet up with the aliens."

"Huh?"

"The aliens."

Marlowe took a fast hit on his drink. "What aliens?"

"We ain't encountered 'em yet, but we're going to. And pretty damn soon, too. I can feel 'em."

Ishmael was too large and belligerent for Marlowe to dare to laugh. A smile was probably not a terribly good idea either. He assumed an air that was part drunk solemnity. ''You can feel them?''

''When I'm out there and the plugs are in and everything about me is tuned into the whole living ship, I empathize. Believe it, buddy, I empathize.'' Ishmael was turning aggressive again. He poked Marlowe with his right index finger. ''I'm aware of everything that is. There's the stuff from the ship and the background stuff from the Earth and the random stuff from space . . . and then there's something else. It's them. It's got to be. There's a pattern to it. I don't understand it, but I know from a pattern. It's like some foreign station bleeding into your audio. Except this is in my head. I've talked to some of the Ivans about it and they say the same thing. The Russians know they're there. And you want to know something?''

''What?''

''When they finally do decide to show themselves, they're going to cream our ass.''

''How do you figure that?''

''Because they've crossed the galaxy, and we're too dumb to be out here on our own.''

''Damn.'' Marlowe wasn't too drunk to notice the gray-and-black-uniformed figures that had sauntered through the entrance. Two more came through afterward. He flashed a warning glance at Ices, but she'd already seen them. Ishmael caught the look.

''You on the lam or something?''

''Something.''

Ices was at his side. Another pair of IPs had come into the Golden Slipper. All six moved slowly through the crowd making a fairly detailed inspection. Conversation fell away, although Sateen Wallis continued to pump from the sound system. One of the cops was scanning with something about the size of a flashlight.

Ices looked anxious. ''It's a makescan, probably hooked into the wanted list.''

Marlowe was suddenly sober. ''Then I'm dead.''

''Pull your cap down over your eyes. The makescan isn't too sophisticated. The peak may throw it off.''

Ishmael spread a pair of massive hands. ''Anything I can do?''

Ices suddenly grinned at him. "You still love me?"

"Sure."

"Start a fight for me."

Ishmael faced Marlowe. "I'll whup his ass good."

"Not him, you idiot. I need a diversion."

As diversions went, it was a classic. A slight young boy with too much makeup was edging away from the police. Ishmael grabbed him and hurled him into a pair of leather-and-chains muscle builders. Before those two could work out what was going on, he waded into them swinging with both fists. A wide circle instantly formed around the fracas. People were yelling advice and offering odds. The cops were trying to push their way through.

Ices put an arm around Marlowe. "Lean on me. Pretend you're drunk and keep your head down."

It wasn't too hard.

The fight proved to be very mobile. The two muscle builders, when they had sorted themselves out and pushed Ishmael off them, picked him up and hurled him bodily into the front-row spectators. Half the crowd surged backward while those at the back pressed forward. The confusion took Marlowe and Ices most of the way to the nearest exit. The cops were clubbing the unfortunate muscle builders and fighting with people in the crowd. With one backward look, the two of them slipped away.

Ices deemed it inadvisable to take the bus, so they made their way slowly and carefully down to the hub of the rotating section. At the point where the transfer was made to free-fall, they had half expected to run into a patrol. But there were no police at all. From an overheard conversation, they learned that the police had been there but had been called away to a riot in the Golden Slipper. Ices decided that everything was going according to plan.

It would take them at least two hours to get back to Ices's lair on foot, so she led him deeper into the new free-fall section. "There's a tube of overnights sealed to a lock on level seven."

Marlowe had drunk too much to coordinate himself in free-fall and progress was slow. Along the way they passed a small troop of chimpanzees wearing chest harnesses to which were attached what looked like computer keypads. Marlowe stared at them in total amazement, half convinced that he was either losing his mind or going into DTs.

"What are those?"

"Chimps."

"That's what I thought. What are chimps doing on a space station?"

"They work here. There's a lot of chimps up here. They're really agile in free-fall and they do a lot of the simpler construction tasks. Of course, there's been a bit of genetic tailoring. They're not ordinary chimps."

"What are the keypads around their necks?"

"That's how they communicate. Not even the geneticists could get them to talk, but they've always been able to tap out their own computer language. Yerkish was invented back in the twentieth century when the first experiments in monkey communication were going on."

The chimps seemed to resent the two humans staring at them. They chattered at them briefly, then swung off down the corridor. They moved through zero gravity with amazing ease and grace.

Marlowe shook his head. "Monkeys."

The overnight tubes turned out to be smaller versions of the temporary environments in which Ices and so many of the lower-echelon workers lived. The capsules were tiny, each little more than a double bunk with a sealed plastic pod around it. There was so little headroom that a man couldn't stand upright. Most of them were in use, and Ices and Marlowe had to go some distance down the access conduit before they found one that was vacant. When they had pushed their way through the flap and privacy-sealed it, Marlowe floated in a hunched, almost fetal posture and slowly looked around. To say the least, it was minimal.

"Damn, it's like a flop-o-mat back on Earth. I've slept off more than a few drinks in those pay coffins."

"It's much the same principle. The drunks use them when they can't make it back to their regular barracks, and the prostitutes bring tricks here."

Marlowe placed one hand flat on the wall. "I can't get

used to the idea that there's nothing but empty space beyond this."

"It's pretty thick plastic, what with the radiation shielding and all. It doesn't hole easy."

"Still seems pretty flimsy to me."

"Don't think that way. It'll make you crazy."

"Play the odds, right?"

"Right."

Ices had let her gold high heels float free. She was sliding down the fastener on her black bodysuit. She must have seen the surprise on Marlowe's face because she grinned at him. "Why don't you get rid of your clothes and come over here? I'll teach you how to make love without gravity."

Marlowe could not deny that it was a truly unique experience, or that Ices was the best teacher that he could hope to find. Without the pull of gravity pressing them together, there was an intense delicacy about the way their bodies moved against each other. Without concepts like up and down, no one was on the top and no one was on the bottom. The pressure of flesh on flesh was a matter of their own control and imagination, and not something dictated by planetary forces. He discovered that they could couple in ways that he would never even have conceived of back on Earth. Planetside, the idea that one took flight during moments of sexual exultation was a matter of illusion. Here in orbit, they truly flew.

When they had finished, Ices moved away from Marlowe and formed her legs into a full lotus, steadying herself with one hand. She reached for her discarded bodysuit and fumbled in the pouch. She produced a single cigarette and a lighter. "You want this?"

"How did you know I smoked?"

"I saw your data."

Marlowe floated puffing on a cigarette. Just one arm hooked through a safety web. He was completely at ease. So at ease, in fact, that he was taken completely by surprise when Ices moved up beside him, the look of sleepy satisfaction gone from her eyes and her expression all calculation.

"So, Marlowe, tell me everything you know about Christine Stavers."

Sadly Marlowe added Ices's name to the list of those who had tried to manipulate him.

TEN

"THEY SHITHEADS CALLIN' THEMSELVES ADMINISTRAtion, that Brother Raxalt who think he know everytin', they don't really know nothin'. They talk about control, but all they really doin' is promotin' anarchy. Not that Italman have anythin' against anarchy, you 'stand. Anarchy a natural organic state. This anarchy has too much bullshit conflict. All they shitheads know is conflict. They say they conquering space. They insane. Space will do wit' man whatever space want. Jah know."

Marlowe nodded sleepily.

"Jah know."

Space was certainly doing what it wanted to with him. He had been stoned for four Earth standard days and he really didn't give a damn. After he had finally left Ices, he had been shuffled from one segment of the resistance to the next, slipping farther and farther down the social scale until he finally came to rest deep in rocket-trash country in a tube where most of the inhabitants maintained sufficient detachment from reality not to give a damn either, particularly regarding whether or not Marlowe was an administration spy.

Italman talked slowly and softly almost as though he were ruminating to himself. It was hard to tell exactly how old he was. His matted, graying dreadlocks stood out around his wrinkled walnut face and stooped shoulders like some exotic, undersea plant that had a life of its own. His only garment had once been a tan jumpsuit, but now it was a darned and patched coat of many colors. He carried a worn staff of dark wood topped by a carved Lion of Judah. There was, as far as Marlowe could see, no way that the man could be a day under seventy. When Marlowe asked, he always got the standard knowing smile and the standard answer.

"Italman always been here. Italman come from space."

Marlowe was rapidly finding out that the tubes of the rocket trash were a world within a world, the Casbah of the orbiting environment. A large percentage of its inhabitants had little or nothing to do with either RAMco, the Raxalt administration, or even the installation's financial superstructure. Most had come up on the basic labor contract, but somewhere along the way they had discovered that there were better, although less legitimate, ways of making a living. Others had slipped in through the gray areas of what was known as the free enterprise backup clause in the original RAMco charter. RAMco was, after all, a capitalist corporation and, in the early days, it had been decided that there had to be a place in space for the small-time entrepreneur. At first, it had been a matter of small businessmen who bought shuttle space to import small dirtside luxuries that they sold to the general population. Later the clause was invoked to bring in the dancers and the prostitutes, the gamblers and the fortune-tellers, and all the others who catered to the more basic needs and preyed on the gullibilities of this rough-and-ready pioneer community. It provided natural cover for drug dealers and stim runners. All followed the natural lure of the uncontrolled life in the tubes. A sprinkling of spacecrew who had either jumped ship or become bored with waiting for the next one, along with individuals like Italman, for whom there was no logical explanation, made the group that had come to be known as the rocket trash. Marlowe was the newest arrival, coming there by a kind process of social osmosis that had seemingly brought him to his own level. He had finally found tolerance and, after learning that Ices had set him up with a sizable credit of phony backpay, even a ready welcome.

There had been numerous attempts to clear the rocket trash over the years, but none had amounted to anything more than a temporary inconvenience. Their hold was too tenacious and their turf too hard to police. The tubes had been illicitly extended, and hidden conduits and transfer tubes had been patched in until they had become as complicated as the catacombs of ancient Rome, the sewers of eighteenth-century Paris, or the shanty towns around contemporary Calcutta or Mexico City. Marlowe suspected that Raxalt and De Kuyper probably accepted the situation because in some ways it actually suited their purpose. When three of their major industries were drugs, prostitution, and booze, the rocket trash quite literally supplied the opium to the people.

Italman was once again filling his pipe. Marlowe wondered how the cranky air-circulation system coped with the enormous quantities of ganja smoke that were generated in the rastafarian barbershop. Hair cutting in space was a complicated business of helmet trimmer and suction tubes. Hair trimmings in free-fall were a serious hazard. Why a sect that was so particular about not cutting its own hair should set up in the hairdressing business was probably something else that Jah knew. It did, however, provide a perfect front for an extensive ganja distribution business. The rastas were reputed to have maybe a dozen pods full of flourishing, climbing, free-fall mutant marijuana.

The rasta barbershop was more than just a service—it was a major social interface for this section of tube. It was situated in a pod that was big enough to accommodate the up to a dozen people who could be found at any time of the day, sucking down Red Stripe beer and filling and passing the electric ganja pipe.

The pipe was coming to Marlowe. He wondered if he should take another hit. Maybe he'd had enough. Ah, what the hell. A young man was strapped into the chair having a wooly afro conked into a fifties process. Seven other men lounged or floated in the haze, and a young woman in an extremely tight red bodysuit played a miniaturized lexilux.

Italman was gathering himself together in preparation to leave. Everything that Italman did involved a considerable amount of improvised ceremony. Packing his ganja bag and personal pipe was a major ritual all on its own.

"There little gal down along th' tube need considerable spiritual instruction from Italman. Jah know Italman is the servant of his flock."

There were volumes of rumor regarding the diligence with which Italman served the young women in his flock who seemed in need of spiritual instruction, and his parting statement raised some wry grins among the men. The woman in red laughed out loud. "You should watch that instruction, old man. You don't want to overdo it."

Italman's eyes twinkled as he floated to the exit trap. "Don't fret you pretty head about Italman, daughter. Jah give me my strength."

After the old man had left, there was a certain amount of reshuffling in the barbershop pod. Winston, who took it upon himself to keep things moving along, floated by Marlowe. "You want another beer?"

Marlowe thought about it and shook his head. "No. I figure I'll hit a couple of other joints and see what's doing."

"You be back later?"

"Most likely."

"Take it easy then."

Marlowe pulled himself lazily along the conduit. He'd left the barbershop on impulse, with no real idea of where he was going. If he had any complaint about his exile among the rocket trash, it was that his life lacked any sense of purpose. All he could do was to keep moving and become as faceless as possible. He was spending time moving slowly from bar to shebeen to barbershop. This particular day's wandering first took him down the long, broad access tube known as Buck Rogers Boulevard, which served as the main artery to a whole cluster of residential units. This was the closest that the rocket trash came to having an entertainment strip of their own. The regular panel lighting had been ripped out all along the hundred meters of its length and replaced by makeshift mood glow. The walls were daubed with garish murals. Buck Rogers Boulevard was where the small-quantity drug dealers plied their trade and the hookers who couldn't or didn't want to go into the places like the Golden Slipper where the IPs had easy jurisdiction cruised for tricks. Marlowe had yet to cease being amazed at the contortions into which the girls could put themselves as they tried to attract customers in the free-fall environment. Each time he ambled through there, he was momentarily tempted to spend a little of Jimmy Dean Garvin's back pay. Some of the women were truly magnificent as they drifted sensually in among the potential clients like dolphins frisking in and out of schools of more pedestrian fish. The temptation never lasted very long, however. Ices had left enough of an afterglow to keep him going for a while. There was also the nagging fear that the tubes might be breeding their own unique diseases.

Buck Rogers Boulevard led inevitably to the Mekon Bar, where the lights were green, the drinks were green, and the patrons were expected to be seated at tables, lapstrapped to their chairs while the waitresses floated free in among them. The seating rule, which was supposed to stop free-fall brawls, gave everyone a conspiratorial air. Marlowe didn't stay very long at the Mekon. The atmosphere was too much for him, making him think of informers and police spies. It reminded him of the Berlin of *The Threepenny Opera*. Maybe it was just the layout, but the people who gathered there looked as if they were selling secrets or planning heists. There was also the matter of the bathtub gin served in green squeeze bottles. Marlowe wished that he could go back into a place with gravity like the Golden Slipper. He really did prefer his whiskey to lie down in the glass so he could sip it, rather than having to be forced through a tube. He didn't think that he could manage the Golden Slipper on his own. He had to assume that the police were still looking for him and he knew that he had no one like Ishmael to count on for a diversion.

From the Mekon Bar, he headed deeper into the less organized areas of rocket-trash country where the attractions were a good deal more minimal. As he moved toward the outer ends of the tubes, there was no mood glow or the good-looking, athletic whores. Instead of bars, there were open pods where hooch was sold and loitering was the most popular occupation. These places tended to become the turf of the various rocket-trash subgroups. In this, it wasn't unlike the Zone, although the Zone was never so lacking in the minor comforts. He passed by a place that was filled with a huddle of black-dressed young people in their mid to late twenties, most of whom had shaved heads and pale, vacant expressions. They appeared to be dedicated to the idea of becoming detached from reality by inhaling desperate, mind-wrenching gulps of a cocktail made from industrial chemicals that was known as Reducer Number 9. Some of this lost generation had even carved small crosses into the middle of their foreheads. Marlowe figured that they had to be less spectacular cousins to the urban vampires or the bands of mansonards who roamed the deepest badlands terrifying the vags and the joads and indulging their preoccupation with rape and murder and, according to rumor, the occasional piece of cannibalism and the odd human sacrifice. These sad specimens probably weren't nearly that dangerous, but they still weren't the kind of company that he was seeking.

He also didn't linger long at a pod where a bearded, balding man with his hair scraped back into a straggly ponytail insisted on reading dreary blank verse to an audience of a dozen or so near-comatose drunks while a fat couple fornicated in midair behind his head and provided him with an accompaniment of wheezing grunts. Each time Marlowe ventured into these far ends, he was beset by the question of how these misfits had managed to get into space in the first place. Or was it space itself that made them crazy? Marlowe did have the answer to the set of companion questions: Why didn't they go back to Earth? Wouldn't it be easier to take their weirdness and their addictions back home where tubes didn't rupture and solar radiation didn't burn relentlessly into their inadequately shielded cells? The truth was unpleasantly simple. They couldn't. These people in the far end were the human flotsam of the orbiting environments. They were the winos and burnouts of the new frontier. They didn't pack calcium and exercise the way Ices had told him to do. They had sunk back into the ease of free fall and atrophied. If they returned to earth gravity their bones would snap. They were condemned to spend the rest of their lives amid drifting garbage in these plastic tubes. Before humanity even had so much as a foothold in the universe it had started exporting its problems. If Raxalt wanted to get rid of his unwanted, he couldn't ship them back. He had no choice but to cut their habitations loose and let them float off toward the sun. Marlowe didn't doubt that the man had given the idea some consideration.

A life of wandering aimlessness, despite its initial appeal, quickly became tedious and then headed in the direction of depressing. Marlowe wished that he could go and see Ices, but she had warned him that she had to do some work for the administration and that he shouldn't contact her. Eventually he found himself homing once again on the rastafarian barbershop. Very little had changed since he had left. The stoned figures still floated in limbo, passing the pipe and drinking Red Stripe. The Dublords still boomed from the sound system. The woman in the tight red bodysuit was no longer there and Italman hadn't returned. Marlowe was sorry to see that the woman had gone. The barbershop tended to be overbearingly masculine. The rastafarians still saw themselves as patriarchs of the old school. Marlowe anchored himself in a corner and looked around for Winston, but Winston wasn't there. The beer was being sold by a tall dread whom Marlowe hadn't seen before.

He had just popped the seal on his beer bag when the flap opened and the woman in red floated back into the pod. Marlowe was mildly surprised when she took up a position beside him. Previously, she had never given him a second glance.

He nodded amiably. "How's it going?"

"You're back here again?"

That wasn't quite the response he'd been hoping for. He shrugged. "I guess I am."

"You've been here a lot in the past couple of days."

"That's true."

"How come we never saw you around here before that?"

Warning signals cut through the haze. He tried to make light of it. "I just moved to the neighborhood."

"Jump ship or just waiting for a berth?"

Marlowe grinned. "It was a bit more complicated than that."

"On the run from the gestapo?"

Marlowe was saved from answering by the tall dread who came by with a beer for the woman in red. He hustled the Red Stripe with a good deal more vigor than Winston had.

"You see Italman down the tubes?" the man asked.

The woman in red shook her head. "I thought he was closeted with some little sweet thing."

"Him call a while ago. Said he comin' on back. Sounded excited 'bout sometin'."

"I ain't seen him."

The tall dread moved on. Marlowe found the idea of Italman using the phone somehow incongruous. He noticed that the woman in red was moving closer to him.

"You got a name, honey?"

Marlowe decided that it wouldn't hurt to use his fake ID. He stuck out a hand. "Jimmy Dean Garvin."

"Stella, honey. You can call me Stella."

There was one of those pauses that follow the breaking of ice. Stella moved even closer.

"Do you have any money, Jimmy Dean Garvin?"

Marlowe was a little relieved that it was a straightforward hustle. He grinned. "Enough to see me through."

Stella put a hand on his arm. "If you need a place to hole up for a while, I can be a great port in a storm."

"I can believe that."

"Nobody need know you were there."

Although he told himself that the proposition was too risky, Marlowe found that he was looking at Stella quite seriously and wondering what it might be like to be alone and naked with her. She must have sensed his indecision, but she didn't press the point; she just floated close to him, smiling, with her hand still on his arm. Her roots were probably hispanic, but it was hard to tell. She had the pallor of someone who never used the sunlight parlors. Her hair was jet black and her lips were sensuous, but although her eyes were large and appealing there was a calculating hardness about them.

"It's something to think about."

"Well, you just take your time and think about it, Jimmy Dean."

Marlowe was doing exactly that. Certainly shacking up with this woman would be a lot more comfortable than aimlessly wandering among the rocket trash. Something inside him told him that Ices wouldn't approve of this kind of an arrangement, but something else countered that it was his responsibility to look after number one and not to be seeking Ices's approval at every turn. At the same time, caution reminded him that all this was only relevant if the offer was on the level. For all he knew, she might be intending to turn him in to the gestapo or have three henchpersons waiting somewhere to mug him. He took a deep breath. If she was simply shilling for muggers, she probably wouldn't be working out of the rasta barbershop.

"You know, a spell of peace and quiet might not be such a bad idea."

The vision of erotic peace and quiet abruptly burst as Winston came through the door flap. His normally easygoing face was a mask of restrained fury.

"They killed Italman!"

There was the silence of total shock. When the questions came, they were faltering.

"Who'd kill Italman?"

Winston cracked himself a beer. He looked like a man who wasn't going to hold together much longer. "It was the kill crews. He was jumped from behind and strangled. That's the way they always do it."

"What did Italman do? Everybody loved him."

"That's exactly why they killed him. It's a message to all of us. They telling us that we better mind our manners because no one is safe."

There was only one dissenting voice. "This is all supposition."

Winston rounded on its owner. "Oh, yeah, shithead? You got a better idea?"

The dissenting voice shut up. Others were now clamoring for details.

"Who found him?"

"Where was he killed?"

Winston was shaking his head. "People are angry. They're mad as hell. There's a lot of them saying they're not going to take it anymore. A crowd's starting to gather down on Buck Rogers. There's talk about making a move on the administration wheel."

The barbershop was filled with angry murmuring. Most of the men were getting ready to leave. They clearly intended to go and join in whatever was happening in the tube.

"I didn't know Italman was so important," Marlowe whispered to Stella.

There were actually tears in her eyes. "Folks out here loved Italman. He was like . . . I don't know . . . a figurehead, a mascot. He was a fixture. He'd been here forever. Those bastards have gone too far this time. They knew he wouldn't hurt a fly."

Stella had anchored her feet and was easing into a standing position. Everyone was moving toward the exit flap. Marlowe looked up at her.

"What are you going to do?"

"I'm going down the Buck with the others. Are you coming with me?"

Marlowe reached for a handhold. "I guess so."

Clearly the deal that he and Stella had been about to consummate had been put on hold until after whatever was going to happen had happened. Although he wasn't overly anxious to witness his first riot in space, he decided that the best thing was to tag along. He followed Stella and the others down into the conduit. As they made their way toward the center of the tube complex, they encountered a growing number of people all going in the same direction. The entire population seemed to be on the move. A good number of them were carrying clubs or bats or heavy wrenches. The anger was contagious. Marlowe had hardly met the old rasta, but even he could feel a sense of outrage. Also contagious was the euphoria that comes when those who have previously felt powerless are pushed too far and finally take matters into their own hands. Not that Marlowe wasn't without misgivings. If he knew anything about De Kuyper and his police methods, events were moving relentlessly toward a violent and bloody confrontation. He didn't feel that it was his fight, but he also didn't want to draw attention to himself by turning around and going against the flow.

By the time they arrived, the gathering crowd had completely filled Buck Rogers Boulevard and was backing up into the narrower connecting tubes. It was in one of those that Marlowe and Stella, Winston, and the other men from the barbershop came to a halt, unable to go any farther. They couldn't see what was happening on the main strip, but the noise told the whole story. The angry shouts seemed to go in cycles, rising and falling in volume and intensity. It wasn't possible to hear exactly what was being said, but by the tone of the harangues and the response of the crowd, it was clear that nobody was preaching moderation. The people of the tubes were working themselves up to a point where they were ready to abandon all restraint and go on the rampage.

The noise in the main tube was building to a crescendo. There was chanting.

"Fight back! Fight back!"

Even in the small tube there was pushing and jostling. Everyone was ready to go. There was a roar as the dam burst.

"We're moving!"

Then there was no turning back. Marlowe was caught up in the general excitement. The crowd wanted action. The rocket trash was going to stomp some ass and nothing was going to stop them.

"Fight back! Fight back!"

They were into the Buck and moving fast. Grim-faced space crew and construction workers moved side by side with the hustlers and bums from the far ends. There was a fair sprinkling of real weapons in the mob—nonlethal bop guns, stunners, and electro prods. Knives, saps, and brass knuckles were no doubt concealed under clothing. Marlowe was relieved that he was well to the rear. The front rank of the mob would run headfirst into whatever defense De Kuyper might have organized and, in the confined spaces of the environment, they were liable to be creamed.

Marlowe's group had passed through a jammed airlock

and into the main structure of the installation. The chanting went on and on.

"Fight back! Fight back!"

They were through another lock and into a wide, curving corridor. As the crowd pressed forward, Marlowe found that he didn't have to bother with the clumsy Velcro walking. He simply let himself drift and allowed the momentum of the crowd to carry him along. Then the tone of the shouting up front abruptly changed. The chanting stopped. The forward movement came to a stumbling halt. People anchored themselves and waited. The front ranks had run straight into the first line of administration defense and the sight of fifty or more IPs in full armored suits with the helmets locked down had somewhat cooled their ardor. The recoilless, pump-action riot guns that each one carried cooled it considerably more—they fired only lowload plastic pellets, not sufficiently powerful enough to rupture the skin of the environment but more than enough to make a mess of unprotected human flesh. For long minutes, the two sides simply stood and stared at each other. The tube people were angry, but nobody was quite ready to be the first to dash themselves on the line of armor. The standoff didn't last, though, and the crowd wasn't slow to start pumping itself up again. Taunts were shouted. A new chant started up.

"Murderers! Murderers! Murderers!"

Somebody in the second rank threw a bottle. Other missiles followed. Those in the rear started scavenging for construction materials, anything that could be thrown. The IPs retreated a few paces in the face of this hail of debris and a loud cheer went up. The victory proved to be short-lived. The cheers turned to panic as the police charged. People were scrambling back down the corridor, blundering into those who were still pressing forward. The shots were followed by screams. Marlowe glanced at Stella.

"Let's get the hell out of here! This is turning into a massacre."

The corridor was a nightmare of confusion as the police pressed forward. With no up and down, fleeing people came from all angles. Free-fall skills were forgotten as the panic set in. There were more shots. Marlowe lost his footing and plunged headlong. He cannoned off a rigger who was also trying to get out of the way.

Moments later, the explosion ripped through the corridor.

In retrospect, nobody seemed to know how or why the explosion was triggered, or even which side was responsible. Those closest to it were killed immediately by the blast. Still more died of explosive decompression as they were sucked out of the widening hole in the outer skin. A number of the IPs were also sucked out, but they were protected by their suits. The shockwave and the pall of smoke initially rushed up the corridor but was instantly replaced by a howling, hurricane-force gale as the environment's atmosphere started venting through the hole. Marlowe, already without an anchor, was blown along by the rushing wind. He grabbed for a handhold, but to no avail. All around him, others of the crowd were being blown toward the rupture point. Alarm sirens were screaming and warning lights had begun to flash. Airtight doors were closing all down the corridor. For a horrified moment, it didn't look to Marlowe as if they were going to close in time to prevent him from being sucked out into the void. There was still a six-inch gap when he slammed into the doors. Somebody else slammed into him. For a second or so, it seemed as though an irresistible force was going to drag them both through, and then the doors sealed themselves. The horrible suction stopped. The dazed rioters started to sort themselves out and nurse their bruises. Nobody could quite believe that someone had deliberately damaged the outer skin. The act went against everything that they knew and believed. Whatever the internal problems, the cardinal rule was always observed: One never compromised the environment.

For the next three days, the entire population seemed to be in shock. No work was done, and only the essential services were maintained. Ships stood idle in matching orbit. Microwave power was no longer beamed to the grid on Earth. The only construction crew who showed up on shift was the emergency team that had been designated to patch the hole caused by the explosion. It was part strike and part a period of mourning. The administration announced that the explosion had been caused by subversives, and the subversives countered that it had been an act of the administration, but these were about the only aggressive posturings. There were no more disturbances, and the gestapo stayed out of the tubes. Both sides in the conflict appeared to have decided that events had run completely out of hand and that there had to be a degree of pullback and face saving—for the time being.

The environment was unnaturally quiet. There was a good deal of drinking going on, but it was grim and introspective. The death toll of the rioters stood around thirty. It was impossible to get an exact count because any number of those sucked out of the puncture could have been far-enders without legitimate ID. Four IPs had also been killed. For a while, the funeral of Italman looked as though it might provide the next flash point, but, despite the large crowd, it went off quietly without either incident or provocation by the police, and the ancient rastafarian's body was allowed to drift to the planetary atmosphere where it flared briefly and was gone.

Marlowe had temporarily moved in with Stella. She had proved as good as her word and, in return for a sizable chunk of Jimmy Dean Garvin's back pay, had started taking care of him in every sense. It was hardly a riotous episode, but that was due more to the somber times than any lack of enthusiasm on Stella's part. He had tried to contact Ices on a number of occasions, but all internal communications were down. Although Marlowe was comfortable, he still spent too much of his spare time wrestling with the problem of how he was going to get out of the mess that he was in. Stella's advice was to get off the RAMco installation.

"If you've got enough money, you can get on a ship, no questions asked."

"I could get back to Earth?"

"Maybe not to Earth. I doubt you'd be able to buy your way through the dirtside customs."

"So where do I go?"

"Out. You could go deep space, or head for the moon, or even Mars."

"Mars? Could you see me out there on Mars with the last of the commies?"

"Maybe not. You want me to find out what I can?"

"Sure. I've got to get off this damn thing one way or another." Marlowe certainly didn't relish the idea of going deeper into space.

On the fourth day after the confrontation with the police, people started to drift back to work. The loading crews were the first, followed by the construction workers and the communication teams. On the fifth day, the microbeam was turned back on again, and by the sixth things were superficially back to normal, although in the tubes there was still a seething resentment that would certainly burst eventually. With communications back online, Marlowe once again tried to contact Ices, but she was still unavailable. It made him a little uneasy. He felt a little as though he was being abandoned to his fate.

By the seventh day, Stella was starting to make noises about how, even though the money was nice, she hadn't expected him to take up permanent residence. The time was coming when Marlowe was going to have to confront the problem. The work stoppage had seriously disrupted ship departures, and the only craft leaving that might have taken him aboard was an ice prospector headed for the asteroids. That struck Marlowe as just too rugged. There had to be a better solution.

As had happened so many times since he had left the Zone, it turned out that the problem came along and confronted him. It arrived in the form of four men. Two of them Marlowe already knew. The easygoing Winston and the chronically suspicious Aman made an unlikely team. Marlowe hadn't been aware that the rastas and Aman's group of subversives were in any way connected. The other two, Marlowe would later discover, were John Single Cloud, a hawk-nosed, full-blood Algonquin Indian who was a key organizer among the construction workers, and Moe the Roller, a man mountain from the far ends with a reputation for violence, but also one for being nobody's fool. They came through the entrance flap to Stella's pod like something out of a gangster movie.

"You're coming with us, Garvin."

"What did I do?"

''It's not what you did, it's what you're going to do.''

Marlowe's stomach was churning. He slowly got to his feet. A little surprisingly, Stella seemed almost as scared as he was.

''You're not going to hurt him, are you?'' she asked.

''Not if he behaves himself,'' was the answer.

ELEVEN

"WE ARE GOING TO KIDNAP CHRISTINE STAVERS."

Marlowe pursed his lips and said nothing. How was it that so many lunatics didn't feel that they could get on with their fantasies without involving him in them? He was back in the graffiti-daubed pod where they had first brought him after saving him from execution. There were a dozen people crowded into the confined space. As far as Marlowe could see, they were representatives of most of the major shades of opinion among the opposition to the Raxalt administration. The air was heavy with a feeling of unease and suspicion.

"Don't you have anything to say, Marlowe?"

"I think you're probably crazy, but that's not the point. All I want to know is why it has to involve me."

A swarthy construction worker was glaring at him. "You came here with her."

"That's not strictly true. I was brought here with her. It was altogether against my will."

"Don't split hairs, Marlowe."

Ices seemed to be presiding over the meeting. Marlowe was somehow disappointed. He had expected more of her than this loony-tune scheme. He looked slowly around the gathering. De Kuyper would love to know that all his subversives had put themselves in one basket.

"I don't even know why you want Christine Stavers."

"Surely that's obvious. She's of great value to Raxalt, and if we have her, we have a valuable bargaining chip."

Marlowe was close to losing his temper. Only the huge presence of Moe held him back. He pointed at Ices.

"You, at least, know that's not true. You've seen all the data. When RAMco grabbed her, they had some idea of sweating all the secrets of Stavers Industries out of her, but they got to her too late. She'd already had the block implant done. They found that if they probed her, they'd only succeed in turning her brains to scrambled egg."

"Raxalt is still holding on to her."

Marlowe sighed. "Raxalt doesn't know what to do with her. He can't probe her and he certainly can't kill her. The estate could be tied up in the Swiss courts for a decade if she died in any kind of weird circumstance. The Stavers systems could even be shut down."

A woman in greasy, shuttle-crew coveralls nodded. "We're blind without the Stavers systems. We couldn't navigate across the room. We'd be back in the stone age."

Aman shrugged. "So we grab her and threaten to kill her. That ought to force some concessions."

Marlowe had had enough. "It seems to me that you cooked up this scheme and now you're looking around for reasons to justify it."

Aman pushed off with one foot and floated threateningly toward Marlowe. "You weren't brought here to have opinions, Marlowe. We're only talking to you because we think you can be of use to us."

"Suppose I don't want to be of use to you?"

Ices intervened. "Marlowe, it's time you woke up to the facts of life. We saved your life and we've kept you away from the gestapo. Now it's time for you to justify your existence."

Marlowe gave up. His shoulders sagged. "And exactly how am I supposed to do that?"

"You'll be along on the kidnapping."

"You've got to be kidding."

"We're deadly serious, Marlowe."

"I was afraid of that."

The reasoning behind the kidnapping may have been tenuous, but the logistics of the actual caper had been put together with some care. Knowledge of the actual details had been restricted to Ices, who appeared to be the central planner, and the five men, including Marlowe, who were actually to do the job. Marlowe was grateful for even this degree of security. It was bad enough to be back in the frying pan without anyone deliberately turning up the heat. He was less happy about the choice of companions. The four who would go with him were the same four who had dragged him out of Stella's pod and brought him to the meeting. He could appreciate having Moe on his side, and John Single Cloud seemed calmly capable. Winston he wasn't sure about. It was hard to tell how someone would react under stress when he had only seen the man in a state of ganja bliss. He was quite sure about Aman—he didn't trust him at all. There were no prizes for guessing who Aman would decide was expendable if it came down to that.

As far as Marlowe could tell, the plan just might work. Christine Stavers was being held in what was called a detention suite on the administration wheel. Presumably Carmila was there with her. That was the first thing Marlowe queried.

"What do we do with the vampire sidekick?"

Aman had his usual answer. "I'm afraid she'll have to be eliminated."

Marlowe was convinced that the man's ancestors had been Islamic terrorists. "I really wouldn't do that. I think Christine will be a lot easier to handle if we bring along her weird girlfriend."

"It's already been decided."

"Then damn well undecide it or you can count me out. I don't particularly like Carmila, but I'm not going to stand by and see her murdered just because you can't resist breaking any available egg while you make your omelette."

Once again, Ices kept the peace. "We'll bring the other woman back, too."

Aman wasn't going to accept defeat gracefully. "It's an added risk."

"It's a worse risk to kill her. It would be better if we had the Stavers woman's cooperation. Our job would be a lot easier if she at least initially believed that we were rescuing her from Raxalt rather than making her our prisoner.''

After the general subversive war council had broken up, Marlowe and the other five had gone straight to Ices's lair where she started outlining the details of the plan. Amid the blinking lights and the flickering monitors, the plot almost seemed plausible. The detention suite was in the same section of the wheel as the hydroponic gravity garden. All that separated the two areas was an atmosphere circulation substation.

''If you go in from the outside, there's a small emergency airlock in the hydroponic area that's hardly ever used. From there it's easy.'' Ices brought up a floor plan on one of the large monitors. ''Just follow the flashing yellow line. You go left out of the lock, through the gardens, through the pumping station, and then Stavers's is door D14 on the main corridor.''

John Single Cloud spoke for the first time since they'd arrived at Ices's. ''How do we know she'll actually be there?''

''According to the gestapo's own log, she and the girl never leave the room. Raxalt's got her almost completely isolated. She's denied all contact, although there is a rumor that she's screwing one of her guards.''

''That sounds like the Christine I know,'' Marlowe commented.

''What does the other one do while all this is going on?'' someone asked.

Ices sniffed. ''I imagine that she either watches or participates. Can we get on with this?''

Everyone nodded.

''So, once you have the two women you go back the way you came and out of the same lock. We've prepared a place to hold them at the far end of tube thirty-six.''

''What happens if they resist?''

''You take Stavers by force and give her a knockout shot.''

''And the other one?''

''Then she will have to be killed.''

Winston was frowning. ''Won't the place be lousy with IPs? There's only five of us.''

Ices grinned. ''That's where I come in. I'm going to

give you one hell of a diversion. By the time I get through, the gestapo will be so busy chasing their own tails that they won't give a thought to Christine Stavers and what might be happening to her. I thought I'd start by fritzing out their communications. After that, I'll plant a few fake emergencies in other parts of the wheel, then, by way of a grand finale, I'll run the tapes of De Kuyper's sex life over the public information channel just as you're going in. If that doesn't do it, I don't know what will.'' Ices looked inordinately pleased with herself.

Moe had a question. ''We'll need untraceable suits. Cop suits would be ideal.''

Ices nodded. ''I've got people working on it.''

Marlowe raised a hand as though he were in school. ''Does anyone mind if I say something?''

''What is it this time, Marlowe?''

''Am I right in thinking that I have to go out into space?''

''That's right.''

''In a spacesuit?''

''Right.''

''We have a slight problem here. I've never been in a spacesuit in my life. I also suffer from vertigo. I'm more than likely to foul up or panic or something. Do you really think that you can risk having me along?''

John Single Cloud regarded him coldly. ''You can be checked out in a suit in a couple of hours. And besides, there's nothing about vertigo in your data.''

Marlowe sighed, ''Then it looks like I'm going.''

When the time came finally to suit up for the mission, the now-familiar sense of unreality had once again overtaken Marlowe. It was the hallucinatory edge that colored his perception and maybe even protected his sanity when his life was at risk. Although he detested being sealed in a spacesuit in an atmosphere that stank of metal, rubber, and polymers, and the emptiness of space brought him close to nausea, neither was an unknown terror anymore. After an afternoon working out beyond the construction base airlock, under the supervision of John Single Cloud and two expert, reliably closed-mouthed riggers, he became reasonably proficient at maneuvering in a spacesuit. He also came to the conclusion that he would never grow to like it.

Marlowe and the other four met in an empty, isolated pod. Five Roland Heavysiders, identical to the suits issued to the police, had already been left there. They had complete IP insignia right down to phony badge numbers. They smelled of new paint. First the men stripped off their inside clothing and put on the undersuits, open-weave longjohns made from specially blended fibers that prevented the suit from sweating up. Next came the suit itself, tough, plasticized, steel-reinforced fabric in two pieces that could be sealed at the waist. Once the neckrings were closed, the bulky backpacks that contained the batteries, airtanks, and the rest of the life-support systems could be attached. Those were followed by the external armor that the police favored. Once the men had pulled on the heavy overboots, they were ready for the helmets with their anonymous dark visors. A half turn locked and sealed the helmet to the neckrings. As it snapped into position, the tiny interior lights around the inside of the visor came on. There was a hiss as the air supply began pumping. Marlowe moved his chin around until the tongue controls and the water-supply nipple were in the right place. Finally the radios were netted.

"We'll be talking on our own private frequency and we'll also have a patch into Ices. She'll be acting as our controller," Aman said.

They separated into pairs and ran through the standard safety checks. Marlowe was glad that it was John Single Cloud who checked his seals and equipment—he instinctively trusted the Amerindian. Finally they picked up their weapons. There were five Mac 8000 recoilless Autoloads. They were squat, square weapons with skeleton folding stocks and blowback vents so they could be fired in free-fall. Marlowe was pleased to see that he was being allowed to carry one.

"What are these loaded with?" he asked.

"Hollow-point plastiques. They'll tear, but they won't puncture."

Aman also hefted a Dygem, weapon-class laser, and Moe packed the two bodybags in which Christine and Carmila would be transported.

The exit from the airlock was a moment of truth. From there on, Marlowe was committed. There was no turning back. Moored outside the lock was a Heinkel jet rail, the simplest form of short-range transport in the space industry, just a single thruster attached to a rectangular metal frame. John Single Cloud tapped Marlowe on the back of his helmet.

"Pay out about a meter of your suit umbilical and clip it to the bars. The rail may not be stylish, but it'll get us there."

The course they took was a good deal longer than just a simple straight line to the administration wheel. They had to follow a long ellipse to match speed with the wheel's rotation and then an angled curve around to the inside of the outer rim to take advantage of the centrifugal pseudogravity. They traveled in silence, and the tension seemed to be intensified by the claustrophobia of the helmet, the sound of their own breathing, and the rhythmic hissing of the airfield. Small plumes of exhaust vapor pumped from each man's helmet.

At last they were alongside the wheel, running close to its inner surface and slightly faster than the speed of rotation. There were a dozen or more suited personnel and just as many small craft in the area, and nobody seemed to pay them any particular attention.

"Airlock coming up."

Winston, who was piloting the rail, cut the thruster and allowed the spidery craft to drop to the surface of the wheel. Moe threw out a magnetic grapple.

"Boot mags on."

Marlowe turned on the electromagnets that were built into the soles of his boots.

"Unhook your umbilicals."

There was an uneasy moment for Marlowe when he was neither secured to the rail nor standing on the surface of the wheel, then his boots made contact with the metal skin and he found that he could stand easily, held down by both the simulated gravity and the magnets in his boots.

"Let's go."

Ices's voice cut in on the radio. "Don't open the lock

until I tell you. I've got to hack it so it doesn't show on any of the function monitors."

"How's the diversion going?"

"It's started. Check one of the public information screens when you get inside." She paused. "Okay, you can open the lock."

Aman popped an inspection cover and hot-wired the lock controls, no easy trick to perform with the bulky suit gloves. The emergency lock was little more than a manhole. They could go through only one at a time, and once inside the lock they had to crouch down in the chamber while the pressure equalized. Marlowe went though second to last, right in front of Moe. He emerged into an artificial jungle lit from above by blue-white growlights. The greenery reached all the way to the ceiling, lush and luxurious, the plants climbing on plastic cables, their roots in long parallel tanks of liquid nutrients. Although the men couldn't feel it inside their sealed suits, the air was hot to the point of discomfort, and the humidity was at saturation point. Their visors fogged up, and condensation streamed down the outside of their space-cold suits.

"Should we take off our helmets?"

"Nah, leave them on. We don't know what we might run into."

Marlowe would have liked a few moments to look around, but the others pressed on determinedly. Rounding the end of one of the tanks, they ran into a gardener in shorts, singlet, and a fiber-helmet. He let out a soft cry of surprise that was clearly relayed into the headset of their suits by the external mikes. The man looked terrified and backed off into the foliage. Marlowe was also startled until he remembered exactly how he looked. There was a lot of power invested in a police spacesuit. They left the hydroponic enclosure, moved into a dark area of quietly humming machinery, then paused in front of the door that led to the main access corridor.

Aman checked in with Ices. "How does it look in the corridor?"

"Seems to be all clear. I've got half the police force looking for a disturbance over on the other side of the wheel."

Winston opened the door a crack and peered out. "Goddamn."

"Is it clear?"

"Yeah, it's clear, but you gotta see this."

"See what?"

"Take a look for yourself."

They moved through the door. As Ices had said, the corridor was empty. There was, however, a public information screen set in the wall right beside the door. It was showing a large color image of Supervisor De Kuyper in full dress uniform. A young woman with long, straight black hair was kneeling in front of him with her face buried in his crotch. She was naked apart from black stockings and purple garters. The police chief was beating her with a braided cat-o'-nine-tails while she squirmed and clutched at him with manacled hands. There was no audio. Moe let out a low whistle.

"Damn."

"This is really going to put the shit among the pigeons."

"Let's keep moving."

Aman turned to Marlowe. "Take your helmet off."

"Why?"

"Because if we all walk in armed and suited up, she's liable to go into shock. At least she'll recognize you."

"And I'm supposed to persuade her that we're the rescue party."

"That's what you're here for."

Winston had moved ahead down the corridor. "Here's D14."

While Aman hot-wired the lock, Marlowe disconnected his air supply and unsealed and removed his helmet. The door slid open. Carmila and Christine were lying side by side on a large double bed. Christine was reading a book, and Carmila was watching a movie. They looked up in surprise and fear as the door opened.

"Marlowe?"

"None other."

"What is this? What are you doing in that suit?"

"We're here to get you out of this."

"Who are these other people?"

"Raxalt would probably call them subversives, but as far as you're concerned they're the U.S. cavalry."

"You're really going to get us out of here?"

"That's the idea."

"Where are you taking us?"

"To another part of the installation where Raxalt and his goons won't be able to find you."

A look of suspicion crossed Christine's face. "Why are you doing this after I as good as left you for dead?"

"I'm just a pawn in the game."

Aman cut the conversation short. His voice crackled harshly from his suit speaker. "We've got to get out of here."

Carmila scowled. "Suppose we don't want to go?"

"I wouldn't advise it."

Christine swung her legs off the bed. "We'll come with you."

"Do you have any other clothes?"

Neither woman was dressed for traveling. Christine wore only a black silk slip while Carmila had on a leather mini and a man's white dress shirt. They both shook their heads.

"This is all they allowed us."

"It'll have to do. Let's go."

Once again, Winston checked out the corridor. "All clear."

Marlowe replaced his helmet. On the screen in the corridor, the young woman was giving De Kuyper a shoe shine with her tongue. Carmila stopped in her tracks.

"What the hell is that, the in-flight entertainment?"

"Just a part of our diversion."

"Some diversion."

Ices cut in on their headsets. "You better start getting the hell out of there. I think the chicken's going to hit the fan any minute."

"What's the problem?"

"They know someone's been dicking around with the command mind. They're in and looking, and I don't have the power to stop them if they come after me. I'm going to have to pull out."

They hurried back down the corridor and through the

pump room. In front of the emergency lock, Moe broke out the bodybags.

Christine looked horrified. "You expect me to get into that thing?"

"We have to go through a spot of vacuum. It's the easiest way."

"You expect me to go into empty space in a plastic bag?"

Carmila joined in. "Those things are for corpses."

Marlowe grinned sourly behind his visor. "Then you should be quite at home."

Aman didn't tolerate humor. He pointed with his gun. "Get in. We don't have the time to argue."

The bags were sealed and then they had to be manhandled into the lock against the pseudogravity. Once out on the inner rim of the wheel, they had to be carried to the jet rail and attached to the frame by a pair of short nylon lines. The men clipped on their own umbilicals, and Winston fed fuel to the thruster. A voice cut in on their headsets.

"This is Ices. The magic's down and we've just about been made. They know that someone or something has gone through that lock and they're scanning to find out what. I can still monitor, but I can't do anything to help . . . uh-oh . . . they know Christine's missing. Get going as fast as you can."

Winston opened the thruster to the max and they lifted away from the surface of the wheel. As they started the curve around the the outside, a large airlock opened in the nearest radial spoke. It was brightly lit from within, and the light streamed out like a searchlight through the expanding cloud of venting vapor. Then the searchlight beam was split by shadows. Six figures in suits and jet packs slowly drifted out. Their suits were police blue. They wheeled away from the lock and gathered speed.

"Gestapo with an after burner. Those swine have got to be after us."

"Can we outrun them?"

"Not a chance. We got too much mass on one thruster."

A second six had emerged from the lock. Winston threw the Heinkel into a tight turn and was heading for the skeletal structure of a half-completed section. Aman was staring backward.

"They're definitely after us."

"All we can do is try to confuse them for a while."

The framework for girders was coming up fast, and Marlowe experienced a moment of panic. Sweet Jesus, they were going to plow straight into it. The rail tilted and they shot through a space with only a meter to spare on either side. Winston spun them upward, twisting in and out of openwork steel.

"Nice flying, rastaman."

Marlowe glanced back. Christine and Carmila, snug in their bodybags, were still in tow behind.

"The bastards are gaining on us."

"Damn."

Six more suits and jetpacks had come out of the lock. A maze of girders was just ahead and Aman took control. "Winston, let us off here. You go on with the women. We'll stay in this construction site and try to hold them."

Winston slowed the rail. The other men had detached themselves and were swinging through the girders, looking for vantage spots where they could anchor themselves. Marlowe bit his lip and unclipped himself from the jet rail. He grabbed a handhold and twisted his body so that his boots could grip. Winston was pulling away. The gestapo were closing fast from the other direction.

Aman was on the headset. "Ices!"

"What?"

"Have they compromised our frequency? Can they hear us?"

"I scrambled your net. You should be okay for a while."

"Okay, everyone listen up. We want to hold them off for as long as we can. Turn out your helmet lights and move back into the deepest shadows. We have to force them to come in and find us. If we get lucky, we may be able to slip away in the confusion."

Marlowe doubted that much luck was capable of existing in one given space, but below him the sun was setting behind a black crescent Earth and soon the environment would be in virtual darkness. Marlowe edged farther back into the maze of girders, shuffling slowly, never risking losing the grip of his boots. He was acutely aware of how clumsy he was in the cumbersome suit and he could all too easily imagine the way the end of a steel spar would rip that suit if he spiraled away out of control. He finally wedged himself in the angle created by three interlocking beams. There he should be almost invisible. He settled in to wait for whatever would happen next. When Aman hissed in his headset, he was actually startled.

"Marlowe, can you hear me?"

"I hear you."

"Do you understand about these 8000s?"

"What about them?"

"They won't breach police armor unless you get real close. Jam the piece in a pig's gut and it'll do just fine, but at long range, forget it."

"So your laser is the only long-range weapon we have?"

"Right."

So you can be the fucking hero, Aman, Marlowe thought.

More cops had emerged from the airlock on the spoke, but the ones who had almost reached the rebels were slowing down, seemingly reluctant to enter the steel jungle of the construction site. They appeared content to spread out and partially englobe the area into which Marlowe and his companions had vanished.

Ices once again spoke in the headsets. "We've had a bit of luck. They don't seem to know anything about Winston taking off with the women. They think that Stavers is still in there with you, and that's why they're holding back. They won't risk killing her. That means they won't use heat seekers."

Aman opened fire with the Dygem in four single-second bursts. The flashes were brilliant green against the steel. The first two were deflected by girders in showers of sparks. The third went wild, but the fourth scored a direct hit. The blue IP suit went pinwheeling backward. An arm was neatly severed. A pink cloud streamed from the gaping hole in the shoulder and left a spiral trail as it spun toward the rotating lights of the big wheel.

The police immediately opened up themselves. A dozen lasers laid fire at approximately where Aman had been. There were gushers of sparks as deflected beams zigzigged among the girders and spatters of hot metal flew like a secondary fusillade. Marlowe curled himself into as tight a ball as the bulky suit would allow. A crackle of static filled his headset—the police had a jam on their communications. The firing stopped. Obviously that distorted yelling had been an order to cease fire. Patches of steel still glowed red in the dark.

John Single Cloud's voice was in the headset. "Aman?"

"I'm okay. Just keep it quiet."

"Watch where you're firing that shit. I don't want you hitting me."

"That's a chance you take."

Marlowe could imagine Aman scuttling along the scaffolding like a monkey or swinging like Tarzan with the laser, clutched in one hand. He was probably enjoying every minute of the action—if, indeed, people like him really enjoyed anything. Marlowe suddenly realized how much he hated people like Aman. They caused all the trouble.

The jammed police net crackled again. The jetpacks briefly blew vapor. The IPs were moving slowly forward.

"Clearing the steel the hard way," John Single Cloud commented.

"Don't fire until you see the whites of their eyes," Moe put in.

"Will you all shut the fuck up?" Aman snapped.

The cops were on the edge of the framework and moving like a closing net. They drifted slowly between the beams on short puffs from their jets, using the small spotlights on the front of their helmets to scan from side to side. Aman let them make a little unhindered progress and then he opened fire again. Once again the laser flashed four times and then he was on the move. This time he claimed three victims. A body drifted close to where Marlowe was crouched. It floated backward with the arms slightly extended, a pink trail coming from a gaping rupture in the spacesuit's chest plate. It slammed into a vertical t-beam and, turning on its momentum, drifted off in another direction. Moving corpses were bad enough, but what really disturbed Marlowe the most was that the whole encounter was being conducted in the silence of space. There was no roar of gunfire, no screams or sobs or curses. The enemy didn't have a face, just a smooth black visor. Death would come with no sound except the meaningless crackle of the headset.

Aman was somewhere else and letting go another burst. The police had stopped their advance. There were more unintelligible orders. They quickly pulled back to beyond the steel. Marlowe looked around for any possible way out. He didn't see one.

The airlock in the spoke was open again. Something was being brought out. It was large and flat and required ten suited figures to maneuver it.

"Damn it to hell! They're bringing up lights."

The flat rectangular object was a bank of free-floating floodlights, the kind that were used for servicing and construction work on the dark side of the station. This battery of quartz halogen lamps would destroy the darkness that was their only advantage.

"We're dead meat."

The lights moved slowly. The unit seemed unwieldy and hard to position.

"Or maybe they're just playing with us."

At last the lights flared into blazing light. Marlowe tried to sink back into the metal cage in which he was wedged, but then he discovered that he was still in a considerable area of inky blackness. The lights had been placed badly and they threw crisscross shadows through the structure that were almost as confusing as total dark had been. The police started to move forward. They were still slow and cautious. The lights were drifting slightly and the shadows steadily moved. Marlowe stayed absolutely still, poised for any chance that might present itself. Aman opened fire again, but this time, when he tried to scoot away, he ducked into a patch of light where he was lethally illuminated. One laser flash brought him down. The others heard a grunted curse in their headsets, and then his body was floating out into open space. Aman was gone.

The police were right in among the steel. Some had discarded their jetpacks and were climbing along the girders. Marlowe tensed. One was coming right toward him. The man carried only an 8000 like Marlowe's and he didn't seem to have spotted Marlowe hiding back in the shadows. He was going to pass directly beneath Marlowe's vantage point. All Marlowe had to do was reach down and place the muzzle of his gun against the man's suit. Marlowe hesitated. It was too easy and too cold-blooded. And then the cop's helmet swiveled up. He started to raise his gun. Marlowe stopped thinking and reacted. He pushed his pumpgun into the IP's face plate and pulled the trigger. Despite the Mac's twin blow-back tubes, the kick almost dislodged him from the steel. The face plate exploded and the man went over backward. Marlowe's suit was spattered with blood, brains, or tissue—he didn't know what. He felt like vomiting, but he fought back the urge. One didn't throw up in a spacesuit.

After the long period of watching and waiting, events were suddenly racing at high speed. Marlowe jacked another round into his gun and started to climb. He swung around a thick main beam and ran almost head-on into a second cop. He fired without thinking. He was too far away to breach the cop's suit, but the blast knocked the man clean off his feet, sending him flying backward, clawing for the controls of his jetpack. He got it going, but he was positioned wrong. He surged forward but immediately impaled himself on the end of a beam. Marlowe turned away. Over on his right, two figures in blue suits were grappling hand-to-hand. One of the figures was huge. It had to be Moe the Roller. Marlowe started scrambling toward them. He spotted a cop with red chevrons on his helmet. Although he was carrying a laser, he seemed to be content to stand and watch the action. His helmet turned and he looked directly at Marlowe. Marlowe fully expected the sergeant to blast him, but instead there was just a crackle in his headset. The noncom must have thought that he was a regular IP. Marlowe raised a gloved hand and tapped the side of his helmet, next to his ear, as if his communications were down. The sergeant seemed to accept this and pointed to the struggling figures, indicating that Marlowe should get up there.

Marlowe went on climbing. He was getting close to the grappling men. The small one had a pumpgun and the other a long butcher knife. Each was trying to get the advantage to use his weapon. There was a terrible irony that with all the tech of the new frontier around them, humans should be reduced to raw cavemen, muscle against muscle. When Marlowe was just a few meters away, Moe managed to free his knife. He slashed savagely at the waist joint of his adversary's suit. It took two hacking cuts before the material split. The contents of the man's stomach exploded all over Moe the Roller's suit. Moe pushed the body away and quickly turned. He was facing Marlowe. He started to lunge with the knife. Marlowe almost lost his footing as he jerked back.

"Moe! No! It's me, Marlowe!"

"Damn it, man, how was I supposed to know?"

They both looked around. There were no police near them. Moe called into his communicator. "John Single Cloud? Are you still alive?"

"Yeah, just about. The gestapo are having trouble telling who's who. I just saw a pig burn one of his own."

"If we could get jetpacks we could maybe fake our way out of here."

"Wait a minute. Look over there!"

"Look where? We can't see you."

"Over by the main tube cluster, look at the big lock."

Moe and Marlowe both turned. Floodlights had come on all around the airlock that John Single Cloud had indicated. Figures were emerging from it like a swarm of multicolored insects.

"What the hell is that?"

Marlowe took a deep breath. "I think it might be the peasants' revolt."

"Marlowe's right. They're coming in this direction."

There must have been upward of fifty individuals in spacesuits. They rode on jetpacks and rails, on loaders and work platforms. There were even rocket trash riding customized funny craft. Marlowe was awed.

"Will you look at those guys?"

As they came closer it was possible to see the infinite variety of styles of spacesuit. There were the color-coded suits of the longshoremen and the construction workers, lighter than those of the cops but still seriously armored. There were the lightweight flexisuits favored by space-crew; some, probably from out of the far ends, were fancifully decorated with elaborate paint jobs and added crests or horns. A few suits were so old that they must have dated back to the twentieth century, huge, bulbous Masseys and Zims with enormous, partial-bubble head-pieces. Most of the suits' owners carried weapons—they ranged from pipes and bats to lasers, minidrivers, and portable welding units. The rescue force may have looked bizarre, but they were loaded for bear.

The cops had also observed the approaching crowd, and there was a long burst of scrambled communications. The cops in among the steel began to move back to open spaces. Those who were already there, clustered around the bank of lights, had formed themselves into a tight defensive group. The mob from the tubes was spreading out into a wide and threatening front. The entire force of police gathered around the lights, which dimmed and went out. Towing the unit behind them, they started to retreat the way they had come, back toward the lock in the radial spoke.

"Mother of god, they're pulling back, Marlowe. We've won! We've won, goddamn it!"

Moe and Marlowe slapped high-fives. For a second time, Marlowe almost lost his boothold. Moe called to John Single Cloud.

"You see that, injun? The bastards are on the run."

"I see it, paleface, and I figure that we ought to get ourselves out of here, too."

They emerged from the steel waving their arms and shouting on an open channel. "Don't nobody shoot! We're on your side! Don't nobody shoot!"

In the middle of the rescue force was a figure in a beat-up red, green, and gold suit. It had to be Winston. Marlowe, Moe, and John Single Cloud made straight for him.

"Is that you, Winston? Did you organize this?"

Winston's familiar throaty chuckle was in their headsets. "Rastaman don't forget his friends."

"But you took time out to change your suit?"

"Didn't want to be mistaken for no gestapo."

They linked arms and hooked on to a passing funny craft. Marlowe suddenly felt like one of the Three Musketeers.

TWELVE

RAXALT HAD AGREED TO NEGOTIATE. IT HAD TAKEN A number of days for him to come to the realization that there was no way that he could intimidate the subversives into relinquishing their position. His police were totally demoralized and couldn't be counted on even if he launched a direct assault into the tubes. De Kuyper had exacted too much personal loyalty from the IPs. Now that he was not only disgraced but also a laughingstock throughout the environment, they were a sullen, leaderless body, unwilling to risk anything for anyone. It wasn't that the environment subscribed to any kind of dirtside morality. Marlowe had first-hand experience that couplings on the new frontier were limited only be the imagination of the participants. De Kuyper's disgrace wasn't a matter of content. Most had seen much worse than his rather archaic sado. It was his style that had brought him down. There was something so absurdly pompous about the examples of his sexual theater that Ices had thrown up on the public screens that nobody could take the man seriously any longer. A police chief who is not taken seriously has, for all practical purposes, lost his power. Raxalt had reacted immediately. He had confined De Kuyper to his quarters and taken personal control of the Installation Police. The action, however, was too late to stop the rot.

It wasn't simply a matter of De Kuyper or even the kidnapping. Christine Stavers was the subversive's trump card, but after the inhabitants of the tubes had come out in open and united revolt, it was very clear that some kind of change had to come to the RAMco orbital environment.

Not that the path to negotiation was easy. There was endless dickering over a multitude of details. One of the main stumbling blocks was the choice of a location for the talks. The subversives didn't trust Raxalt sufficiently to freely enter administration territory, and Raxalt himself flatly refused to set foot in the tubes. The wrangling deadlock threatened to destroy any hope of a settlement until the answer came from, of all places, the Russian colony on Mars. A Martian freighter was due in after the four-month journey from the red planet, and while it was still two days out the commander was contacted and asked if he would be willing to host the crucial series of meetings. The Russians were delighted. Their off-world, communist isolation still maintained a deep appreciation of the romance of revolution. There was also the fact that although the Russians maintained an easy détente with the capitalist space corporations, they were more than happy to see them embarrassed.

Marlowe had no part in the preliminary to-ings and fro-ings. He had neither the skill nor the taste for politics and he was also having far too much fun playing the hero. After what seemed like months of being considered so expendable that his life was constantly dependent on the whims of strangers, it was a heady novelty to have men buy him drinks and women hang on his every word. Stella's attitude had totally changed. Far from indicating to him that he had worn out his welcome, she now tried to be his constant companion, in bed and otherwise. There was no more talk of money. Unfortunately for Stella's newfound passion, she was only one of a number of attractive women who were prepared to bestow extensive favors on the man of the moment and even indulge his bent for threesomes and foursomes. Marlowe didn't mean to be unkind to Stella, but he was well aware that this hog heaven might prove highly transitory and he was determined to enjoy as much of it as he could while it lasted.

Marlowe saw a good deal of his co-heroes, Winston, Moe the Roller, and John Single Cloud. Winston had returned to his normal euphoric self, Moe seemed bent on at least a seven-day, cowboy drunk, and even John Single Cloud was considerably less stonefaced. All through the tubes there was an eager excitement. A change was going to come and could only be for the better. Marlowe hoped that the optimism would be justified. Work was, at best, sporadic. With a new deal expected, nobody wanted to invest too much time in the old one. Essential services were maintained and ships were loaded and off-loaded, but fresh construction was at a virtual standstill. People hung out in the main access tubes with a focus on Buck Rogers Boulevard. The Buck, the bars, and the speakeasies were filled with arguments about how the future would be managed. Judging from the extreme and occasionally violent divergence of opinion, the newly appointed ad hoc steering committee would have a near impossible task in coming up with any kind of consensus. In addition to the loud and almost continuous debate, pressure groups attempted to organize more formal meetings. These, however, were normally doomed to disintegration, as the official speakers were howled down by the unofficial audience. The public TV channels were constantly usurped by individuals who believed that the screen was a medium for public opinion and not just a font of mindless distraction. Marlowe had been particularly irked when, during an afternoon of hanging out in the rastafarian barbershop, an antique copy of *Have Gun Will Travel* was interrupted by an earnest woman with a lengthy diatribe about lesbian rights under any new administration.

"I thought lesbians had rights. What the hell was '97 all about?" someone commented.

"You can never have enough rights," someone else replied.

Ices was in the thick of it. She had moved on to the steering committee as though it was her natural right and appeared to have become its virtual chairperson. On the few occasions that he had seen her, she had been too busy to talk with him at any length. He got the feeling that she wanted to be seen with him because he was one of the ones who had brought in Christine Stavers and forced Raxalt into a position of compromise, but that really she would rather be somewhere else, probably conspiring in a backroom. Power, or actually just the potential of power, had not improved Ices's personality. She was abstracted and gave the impression of seeing no reason to expend energy on being friendly. The fun side of her nature seemed to have been swamped by a tide of grim ambition—unless, of course, it had all been nothing more than a sales pitch. That wouldn't be anything new. If whatever power that might be wrested away from Raxalt was handed over to Ices, Marlowe wasn't too certain about how much of an improvement it might turn out to be in the long run.

The two people that he didn't see were Christine and Carmila. They had been spirited away to some isolated tube where they were being held incommunicado. Marlowe didn't even know exactly where they were.

Half the population of the installation turned out to watch the Russian freighter move into orbit. The observation galleries were packed, and those who had access to suits went out onto the surface of the space station. Even without the fact of it being the location for what might prove to be a historic meeting, the arrival of any of the big Martian ships was an awe-inspiring sight. The *Sergei Eisenstein* was one of the largest and most modern of the ships that made the Martian run. Its overall length, from the squat donut shaped living environment, emblazoned with the red star and the hammer and sickle, to the black bulk of the ion drive was little short of five hundred meters. It had the chunky, slab-sided lack of sophistication that was the hallmark of all Russian space hardware. Although the living environment and the drive were the most impressive features, the greater part of the ship was nothing more than a giant rack frame to which the ore carriers and freight containers were attached.

The *Eisenstein*'s arrival from deep space was nothing less than majestic. The big ship had slowed almost to a stop well before it was visible to the naked eye and it now nosed slowly toward the RAMco station with the exhaust from its retros streaming behind it. Someone had placed smoke markers all around the circumference of the living environment, and these left additional red and yellow trails that were pure show business. A flotilla of small craft had gone out to meet the ship. By far the majority were sightseers who had to stand off while the docking tugs and loading tenders went to work. Moments before the tugs reached her, the *Eisenstein* set off a brief but spectacular display of vacuum fireworks. The Russians seemed bent on creating a lasting impression.

That kind of flamboyance was typical of the Russians on Mars. They seemed to live with a deep-seated, collective insecurity. They were people who had lost a country and found a planet, and they were still very uncertain about what the rest of humanity thought of them. The early twenty-first century had been a time of trauma for Russia, beginning with the series of disastrous reactor failures that had created the vast Russian badlands and triggered the collapse of the Soviet Union as a political entity. With something like sixty percent of the cultivated land poisoned by radiation, the Russians simply couldn't support themselves. The mass migrations to the Martian colony began against a background of famine and the breakdown of civil order.

Marlowe was among the first nonfunctionaries to go aboard the *Sergei Eisenstein*—one of the privileges of being a hero. Winston and John Single Cloud were also along for the ride. Moe the Roller should have been there, but, at the last minute, he had revealed an irrational prejudice against the Russians. Ices was also there with the clear intent of consolidating her position at the bargaining table. There were twenty in the delegation from the tubes, but since they seemed unable to agree about very much in private, Marlowe wasn't sure how they were going to present a united front to Raxalt and his corporate lackeys. Not that Marlowe was particularly interested in highside politics, but he did want to see the interior of a Russian spaceship.

The Russians continued to put on a show. The interior of the ship was strangely ornate; although there wasn't actually wood paneling and a chandelier, neither would have been out of place. The officers' mess had been turned into a combination meeting and reception room and put at the disposal of the two sides from the RAMco environment. The Russian crew, whose tastes more normally ran to bulky sweaters and dungarees, were decked out in their dress uniforms. To Marlowe, they looked a little like airline pilots from the mid-twentieth century. Their powder-blue double-breasted suits had big, padded shoulders, loosely cut jackets, and baggy trousers. There was vodka chilling in ice on a side table.

"I am Star Captain Uri Orloff, and it is my pleasure to welcome you all to the Soviet Spaceship, *Sergei Eisenstein*." Captain Orloff was a small, wiry man with deep, sad eyes and limp dark hair. "I have just received a communication from Director Raxalt. He sends his regrets and says that he has been unavoidably detained. He will get here as soon as he is able."

The delegation members looked at each other with some trepidation.

"What's Raxalt up to now? Is this some kind of trap?"

"Maybe we should get the hell out of here and back where we belong."

Orloff held up his hands for quiet. "Please do not alarm yourselves. I know something of your problems, but I can assure you that Director Raxalt won't try anything while you are in our care. You are under the protection of the Starfleet of the Soviet People, and I think Director Raxalt fully understands what that means."

Ices was in her take-charge mode. "Can a communication link be established with our people back in the installation? There's always the chance that Raxalt will use our absence to try something there."

Captain Orloff was accommodating. "Of course. That is no problem at all. One of my officers will take you to the comm center."

After Ices had left, Orloff smiled genially at the rest of the delegation. "Since we have nothing to do but wait for Director Raxalt, perhaps we should all have a drink."

He led a mass move to the improvised bar. Some of the more conscientious of the delegation forwent the vodka, but neither Marlowe, Winston, nor John Single Cloud were among their number. For those who were drinking, Orloff proposed a toast calling for peaceful co-existence and mutual cooperation between all peoples on all planets. Marlowe raised his glass and threw back the shot in one gulp. The vodka was surprisingly good. One of Orloff's officers proposed a second toast, pledging the Russians' support to the universal struggle for workers' freedom.

The toasts became less and less intelligible as those proposing them grew drunker. Some of the younger officers became bored and wandered over to the bar where Marlowe, Winston, and John Single Cloud were helping themselves to what they had decided was really excellent vodka.

"There's too much bad booze in space."

"Damn straight."

One of the Russians joined the conversation. "You come to Mars. You drink plenty of vodka."

"We'll give it serious consideration, Ivan."

"I am not Ivan. I am Leonid. My friends call me Zoot, though."

"Zoot?"

Despite—or maybe because of—their troubles, the Russians had never really recovered from the rock 'n' roll madness of their swinging nineties.

"Right." Zoot was grinning. "You sticking it to the bosses, huh?"

"That's the general idea."

"I wish your bosses would turn up soon. We all want to go to the station, you know? Buck Rogers Boulevard?"

"You want to meet capitalist girls, right?"

"Right."

As it turned out, Zoot didn't have to wait much longer. It was only a few more minutes before Ices returned from the comm center with the information that Raxalt was on his way. She looked around the room with an expression of distaste.

"So we started hitting the vodka, did we?"

"Not all of us."

"God, you're a motley bunch."

The captain, who by this time had become exceedingly amiable, attempted to put an arm around her. "We drink to peace and freedom."

She evaded him. "Yeah, sure."

Raxalt's entrance clearly was designed to make the delegation from the tubes feel as motley as possible. Preceded by two Russian officers, and followed by a ten-person retinue of police and civilian aides, he swept in trailing a long black cape. The cops were in full dress uniform and even the civilian advisors looked like some kind of neo-inquisition troops in their matching nehru suits. The adversaries seated themselves on two sides of a long conference table that the Russians had provided for the meeting. Raxalt, almost by habit, took control.

"Shall we dispense with the formalities?"

Ices was determined not to be outdone. "I didn't know that there were any precedents for a meeting like this on which formalities could be based."

Raxalt simply ignored her. "I would like to start with the reading of a prepared position paper that comprehensively states the key administration attitudes to the current dispute."

"I thought we were here to talk, not to be read to."

"It would give us a basis for discussion."

"I don't think that we need—"

Again Raxalt ignored her. It was a study in rudeness. "Please read the statement."

One of the civilian aides got to his feet. He was holding a thick binder. Ices started to rise.

"Wait just a minute." Raxalt pinned her with a look. "If this meeting can't be conducted in an orderly manner we might just as well withdraw."

Ices sat down again. "Read the damn paper."

She had lost the first skirmish. Marlowe hoped that she could survive the war.

Even with his hero status, Marlowe hadn't rated a seat at the conference table. He lounged by the bar and watched the proceedings. Pretty soon he wished he were somewhere else. He wondered if the Russians had a boat going across the installation. He wouldn't mind being back on Buck Rogers talking to some capitalist girls. The position paper was lengthy and couched in often incomprehensible lawyerspeak. The gist of it was that, while Raxalt acknowledged that there possibly were some abuses and inequalities in the system that needed reform, he wasn't about to bow to terrorism. He would discuss any of these problems, the majority of which he conveniently blamed on De Kuyper, only after the return of Christine Stavers and the surrender to justice of those responsible for her kidnapping and the killing of his officers. Marlowe wondered if anyone had expected anything else. Ices didn't seem at all surprised.

"Perhaps we should state our position."

Raxalt made a magnanimous gesture. "By all means."

"Please don't patronize me, Director Raxalt."

"I'm sorry. I had no such intention."

"I have no prepared paper, but our position is summed up very simply. If changes are not made, Christine Stavers will be killed."

"Are you threatening me?"

Ices shook her head. "No, but the people who hold Stavers are threatening her, and I can't be responsible."

"I can only repeat that I won't negotiate with terrorists."

A large fuel handler who was sitting at the far end of the table rumbled, "What about the terrorism of your goddamn police?"

One of the civilian aides glanced at Raxalt. He seemed to be asking for permission to speak. Raxalt gave an almost imperceptible nod. The young woman rustled her papers.

"Perhaps we could hear from some of the other delegates and try to get some details of these alleged grievances."

At first, the delegates all talked at once. The slick, neat young woman let them run off at the mouth for a while and then deftly organized them into a running order and started them into a series of lengthy sidetracks. Even drunk as he was, Marlowe couldn't miss the pattern that was emerging. Raxalt's team had taken control of the mechanics of the meeting and were letting the other side wear itself out. Ices must have seen what was happening, but she didn't have the skill or the support to turn the situation around. Raxalt could keep this up until the whole delegation collapsed in on itself.

After five hours of getting absolutely nowhere, the meeting adjourned until the next day. Marlowe wanted to speak to Ices, but she brushed by him without a word. She was clearly furious. He shrugged at her departing back and then fell in with Zoot and a couple of other Russians. The plan was to tour the orbital fleshpots.

Zoot, Maxim, and Blueski seemed bent on proving that the Russian reputation for single-minded and, in the later phases, ponderous drinking was fully justified. The four of them had started at one end of the Buck Rogers Boulevard and methodically worked their way into the tubes, refusing to give any bar, speakeasy, or shebeen the go-by. After the alcoholic prologue on the *Eisenstein*, the still inescapable toasts quickly became quite impenetrable, although peace and comradeship continued to be the big winners. By the tenth port of call, Marlowe was operating in a haze and he knew that in the equivalent of morning he would have a very incomplete memory. After a round dozen visits, Maxim and Blueski peeled off with a blonde and a brunette who seemed equally interested in furthering mutual understanding. Marlowe and Zoot continued to wander until they found themselves, of all places, sitting at a table in the comfortable gravity of the Golden Slipper. Zoot had persuaded Marlowe that no IP was going to bother him while he was in the company of a representative of the glorious Soviet Starfleet. Marlowe was drunk enough to believe him. There was a third person at the table, a rotund Japanese data technician who watched blankly like a glazed Buddha as Zoot tried to promote Mars to Marlowe.

"You're my friend, right?"

Marlowe nodded. He didn't have absolute control of his head. "Right."

"So why you don't want to come to Mars then?"

Marlowe shook his head. "I don't want to go anywhere. If I wanted to go anywhere, I'd want to go home." Marlowe really wanted to rest his head on the table.

Zoot looked confused. "But you tell me earlier you don't have a home. You were pretty upset about it."

"I have a cat."

"You tell me that, too."

Marlowe leaned forward confidingly. "When I say I want to go home, I mean I want to go back down there. I want to go back to Earth."

Zoot was vigorously shaking his head. "Dirtside? You don't want to go dirtside. It's all messed up down there. You an important man. The universe is waiting for you."

"That's all the stinking universe is good for, waiting for you. It's always fucking waiting."

Zoot was trying to attract a waitress. "You come to Mars with me. Shit, we even got the water problem licked."

Marlowe sighed. "Zoot, my old buddy, I got to straighten you out here on one or two things. I'm not an important man. I'm no pioneer. In fact, I'm not sure that I even qualify as rocket trash. I'm a dirtsider and I'm goddamn proud of it."

"But you're here and everybody says you're a hero."

"And I don't even know how that all happened. All I know is that I belong to the old Earth. Not that the Earth ever particularly gave me a break. You ever hear of the Mosconi Act?"

"Sure, it was the way the capitalists dispose of their unwanted workforce when no longer needed. Typical of capitalist corporations. Nothing like that happen under Soviet system."

"That's as may be, but it happened to me. When I was twelve years old, they gave me all the tests. I came out well ahead except they said I had a problem."

"What problem?"

"They said I had an unacceptable attitude to authority. I might be bright, but I was unemployable. I guess I was lucky. I was allowed to take an identity leisure-out. If I hadn't been so bright they might have let me go vagrant or thrown me in a camp. As it was, I came under the get-out section. I might have a guaranteed income in order to continue to contribute to the culture."

"The Ziapsu Plan—income tied to the output of an industrial robot."

"I was among the cream of the useless."

"But all this shit you went through, what about that, Marlowe?"

The waitress put another drink in front of each of them. Marlowe grinned crookedly.

"That's the bitch of it. I really don't know how I got caught up in this mess. The worst thing is that somewhere along the way I actually discovered that I was quite good at it. I thought that I'd go to pieces, but I didn't. Damn it, Zoot. I've killed people, and it still doesn't seem quite real."

"You're drunk, my friend."

"Yeah, I'm drunk."

The next day, Marlowe was too hung over to want to go across to the *Sergei Eisenstein* and spend five or six hours being bored out of his mind. Later he discovered that he had made the right decision. From the stories that came back with the delegation, the second day had pretty much been a rerun of the first, only tempers had been stretched a little more. Day three ran into day four and the talks continued to deteriorate. Raxalt hardly had to prod the delegates—they were doing it all by themselves. In desperation, Ices had attempted to dragoon her people into some kind of order, but that had only caused more hostilities. Maybe she had been around computers too long—she seemed to expect humans to behave in the same way. By the fifth day, the Russians were starting to make wondering noises. Just how long was this going to drag on?

On the night of the fifth day, Marlowe had the idea. He had gone home with a woman called Anita. She had fallen asleep and he was watching *Jazz from Hell* with the sound turned down when the idea came to him complete, fully formed on the half shell. He pushed aside the restraints and sat up. Anita stirred in her own straps but didn't wake. He had to tell someone about it, if for no other reason than he wanted to know whether it really was the answer to the whole thing or if he had merely gone mad. A few days earlier, he might have talked to Ices, but now instinct told him not to do it. Instead he picked up the phone and called John Single Cloud.

"John?"

"Marlowe?" John Single Cloud had obviously been sleeping.

"Can you meet me?"

"Now? I just hit the sack."

"I think I just came up with the answer to the whole deal. I need to run it by you."

"Are you shitting me, Marlowe?"

"I swear to god. I think I've got the solution to all your problems."

"This had better be good."

"Can you meet me at the Mekon Bar in a half hour?"

"I thought you hated the Mekon."

"It seemed like a good place to conspire."

As he dressed, Anita woke up. "Where are you going?"

"I've got to see a man about a revolution."

"Fuck you, Marlowe."

"You just did."

Buck Rogers was quiet, inhabited only by a couple of hookers, a man playing John Coltrane on the saxophone, two Russian drunks, and a figure in black rubber who defied description. There was only a handful of people in the Mekon Bar. John Single Cloud was already there, alone at a corner table. His face was pure granite.

"What's on your mind?"

Marlowe sat in the opposite chair. He fastened the lap-strap. "I think I need a drink."

A waiter placed a green plastic squeeze bottle in his table clip. "You want to pay for a real fresh lemon?"

Marlowe shook his head. He took a long pull at the squeeze bottle. The gin would have been undrinkable if it hadn't been ice cold. He took a deep breath and then slowly and carefully laid out the whole plan. It took an hour to run down all the ramifications. John Single Cloud neither said a word nor even reacted. When he was through, Marlowe sat there with a complete sense of deflation. John Single Cloud still didn't react.

Marlowe reached for a drink. "So? What do you think? Am I insane or what?"

A slow smile spread across John Single Cloud's face. It was like the dawn coming up. "I think you have a workable plan."

"You do?"

"It might even appeal to Raxalt. It at least allows him to retain corporate control. Listen, Marlowe, I'll tell you what I'll do. I'll try to talk to as many of the delegates as I can before they go across to the *Eisenstein*."

"Don't say anything to Ices about this."

John Single Cloud hesitated for only an instant. "If that's what you want."

"I'd rather it came as a surprise to her."

"You don't trust Ices?"

Marlowe shook his head. "It's not that I don't trust her exactly. I don't think she'd sell us out or anything. It's just that I don't know about her motives or what she expects to get out of the situation. I just have this feeling that she's as much in love with power as Raxalt is, and I tend to shy clear from people like that."

John Single Cloud didn't comment, but he was clearly thinking over Marlowe's fears. He unclipped his lapstrap and floated up. "I'll talk to you in the morning."

Marlowe slept very badly. There was too much on his mind. He was up bright and early and met John Single Cloud by the airlock. John Single Cloud looked quite pleased with himself.

"I managed to talk to four of the delegates. Three of them went for your plan right away. The fourth wasn't sure, but even she was willing to listen to anything that would break the deadlock. Do you know Rashid?"

Marlowe shook his head. "I don't think so."

"He's the big fuel handler with the afro. He sits down at the end of the conference table."

"I've seen him."

"He's going to propose that you be allowed to present your plan. Keep an eye out for him."

The atmosphere inside the shuttle that took the delegates and observers to the *Sergei Eisenstein* was grim. Most of those aboard had come to the conclusion that they were participating in an exercise in extreme futility and that Raxalt would never allow the meetings to produce a positive outcome. Raxalt didn't show for the first hour of the meeting, but enough of his aides were there to continue the charade. Marlowe bided his time. He wanted everyone present when he sprung his surprise. When the director did arrive, Marlowe kept a constant eye on Rashid. Sure enough, the big man raised his hand the moment the opportunity presented itself.

"I'd like to move that we listen to what Marlowe has to say for himself. He may have come up with a workable plan."

"Marlowe? A plan?"

One of Raxalt's police escorts leaned forward and whispered something to the director. Raxalt looked sharply at Marlowe.

"This man's a wanted criminal. He was involved in the murder of three of my officers."

"I was only involved because your men were trying to execute me at the time without the benefit of a trial."

"He's also on a Russian ship and you can't touch him," Rashid pointed out.

"That may be true, but I still don't have to listen to criminals."

Rashid wasn't about to let it go. "I still think we should hear what he has to say."

A number of the other delegates were nodding. Raxalt looked questioningly at Ices. Ices shrugged.

"Sure, let's hear Marlowe out. It can't be any more of a waste of time than a lot of the stuff we've been hearing."

Marlowe was given a seat at the table. He looked around for sympathetic faces. He didn't find many. "The basics of this plan are very simple. It all hinges on the formation of an offplanet workers union."

There couldn't have been a more shocked silence if he had suggested that everyone put on Mickey Mouse ears. Now he knew why he had chosen to try out the idea on John Single Cloud. He had known that Single Cloud would hear him through to the end without interruption. Ices was looking at him as if he'd taken leave of his senses.

"A union? Is that your great idea, Marlowe? A union?"

Raxalt said it all. "Labor unions were an aberration of the twentieth century."

Rashid made a dismissive gesture. "That's the corporate line. Corporations can't stand unions."

Marlowe doggedly pressed on. "If you don't like the word *union*, call it something else. Call it a cooperative, call it a friendly society, call it a goddamn craft guild."

One of Raxalt's lawyers openly sneered. "Communism by any other name?"

Out of the corner of his eye, Marlowe could see the

Russians bristling. "I'm not talking communism. The important thing is that the people who work out here in space have a recognized organization to represent their interests. If such an organization existed, I think that we would have a good chance of convincing Christine Stavers to turn over the key patents, systems, and base codes of Stavers Industries to that organization."

The sneering stopped. "Why should she do that?"

"Because it gives her a way out. Right now she's a prisoner. Her back's against the wall. She knows that she can't hold her position. Sooner or later, she's going to have to give up what she has or someone is going to kill her. At the very minimum, her brother and sister will have her declared insane, if they're given enough time. This way, she's relieved of a very dangerous responsibility and, at the same time, she still maintains her grandfather's basic resolve that the supercorps never have an absolute monopoly on space technology."

Ices appeared to be thinking on her feet, debating with herself which might be the best way to jump. "I don't know, Marlowe. I still don't see that Stavers is going to be exactly keen to give up a fortune to some kind of hastily formed labor union."

"That's the point. She doesn't have to. I'm not a lawyer, thank god, but I'm sure it can be structured so that she and the other stockholders in Stavers Industries can be paid royalties just as they are now. Research and development could continue as normal. With the basic patents and data vested in the union, it would be protected from corporate raiding, and the union would have a major lever to prevent the kind of abuses that we have today."

Ices nodded. "It might work."

"It will work."

Raxalt was grim-faced. "Do you really think that I will let this lunacy come to pass?"

"I figure you will when you think about it."

Raxalt raised an eyebrow. "You do?"

"Sure I do. This deal offers you something that you absolutely can't do without."

"This deal offers us precisely nothing. All I need to do is to wait you out."

"That's where you're wrong. You may not be able to grab the Stavers patents, but you will have stability. There are always tensions between labor and management, but out here, it's escalated to armed confrontation. Damn it, man, one bomb's gone off already. How much more violence do you think it'll take before you're removed from the directorship?"

Raxalt didn't say anything, but Marlowe sensed that he was getting through. There was a lot of talk around the table. Ices held up a hand for quiet.

"This is all well and good, but it's all hypothetical until we find out if Christine Stavers is willing to play ball."

Marlowe grinned at Ices. "So why don't we bring her here and find out?"

There was a long silence. Ices started to look flustered.

"I'm not sure I . . ."

"Of course you are. Just get on the horn and have her brought over here."

"How do we know this isn't just an elaborate trick to grab her back again?"

Marlowe lost patience. "Give me a break, will you, Ices? Nobody can negotiate from a position of absolute paranoia."

The rest of the delegates appeared to share the sentiment. Ices knew that she was isolating herself. The fiction that Christine was being held by some mysterious third party was quietly dropped.

"Should I make the call?"

Rashid stood up. "I'll do it."

Christine Stavers was stoned but lucid. Her speech was a little slurred and she seemed unnaturally cheerful. Marlowe wondered what they had been giving her back in the tubes. While the deal was being run down to her, however, she asked a number of pertinent and intelligent questions. Marlowe was considerably relieved. He didn't want the whole thing blown apart because Christine agreed to something while she was out of it on drugs. When the basics were laid out, she smiled at Marlowe. "When did you get so smart?"

"I'm not as dumb as I look."

"Apparently not."

Marlowe made a small inquiring gesture. It was good to be winning. "So?"

"I think I like it."

"Just like that?"

"Agonizing over a decision is either ceremony or weakness. I don't have time for either. I'll need a couple of dozen lawyers, but the principle seems sound. There is one thing, though."

"What's that?"

"If I'm to donate my birthright to this union or whatever you're going to call it, I feel that it would be only fair that I should be given a participating role in the organization."

Ices looked horrified. "A participating role?"

She seemed genuinely shocked. She had fallen into the trap of thinking that because she had been using Christine Stavers as a bargaining chip, the woman *was* nothing more than a bargaining chip. Ices had forgotten that Christine was the granddaughter of the legendary Elias Stavers. It was a bad mistake. Christine seemed to enjoy the moment.

"I think a lifetime on the board or the central committee or whatever you end up with would be adequate. I have to be able to reassure myself that my investment is being properly managed."

Marlowe fed her the line with a smile. "Why would you want to run a union?"

"Because it's the first offplanet union. I'll become the champion of the interplanetary underdog. A Stavers can relate to that."

Ices was speechless. Her fantasy of power was melting in front of her. Christine wasn't finished either.

"It could well assure my place in history into the bargain. Who knows? I might even eclipse my illustrious grandfather."

Marlowe slowly shook his head. He couldn't understand how they all couldn't see it. Power simply wasn't worth all the trouble.

EPILOGUE

MARLOWE EASED INTO THE CONTOUR FRAME AND strapped himself in. There were three other passengers going down the well, two Japanese metallurgists and the engineer of a deep-space ore carrier. The engineer was in a straitjacket. The trithoramine was starting to wear off and he was muttering to himself about how the aliens were on their way. It seemed to be an advanced case of Ishmael's delusion. Maybe all deep-spacers went that way in the end. Or maybe the aliens *were* on their way. Marlowe had reached the point where he was quite capable of believing anything.

After the initial meeting at which his plan had been accepted, negotiations had ground down to the minute details. Study groups and subcommittees were formed, and the whole process looked as though it might take months, if not years, to come to a conclusion. The influx of lawyers was so all-encompassing that a whole new section of the admin wheel had to be opened up to accommodate them. The serious venery and deceit was underway.

There was some consternation as to what should be done about Christine. As a number of people pointed out, there might be individuals in the supercorps who would see the chaos that would result from Christine's assassination as justifiable if it nipped this union business in the bud. Now the boot was on the other foot. Until the plan was fully implemented and the assets legally transferred, the subversives were the ones who needed to keep Christine alive. There was no way that they would be able to protect her comprehensively anywhere on the installation. Given time, a corporate hitman would eventually get to her, and judging by the speed of the negotiations, time was something of which there would be an abundance. It was therefore decided that Christine should take a six-month trip to the asteroids. She and Carmila would become supercargoes of the ice prospector *Gaby Hayes*, beyond the reach of the corporations and protected by a trusted crew. At first, Christine had angrily rejected the idea. She became a good deal more cooperative when she discovered that she and Carmila would be the only women among a crew of fourteen men. A crew had been deliberately selected by no less than Ices to be young, energetic, and interesting. When Marlowe had been told about it, he had merely grunted.

"That sounds about Christine's speed. Maybe she'll run into Ishmael's aliens. She ought to be enough to scare them off."

Even though the plan was basically Marlowe's, he was hardly possessive about it. He had absolutely no desire to see his brainchild take its first steps. All he wanted to do was to get himself back to Earth and he started motivating in that direction. Almost everyone was more than happy to see him go. As he had drawn all of Jimmy Dean Garvin's back pay, Christine had opened a line of credit for services rendered, and Raxalt's people arranged passage back to Earth. He knew that he couldn't go back to the Zone—there was too much risk of lethally disgruntled vampires. There were other places, though, where a forties leisure-out could hang his hat. He would get his cat and his belongings. Beyond that, he didn't know. He wanted to be anonymous, just to fade into the background. He'd had more than enough excitement to hold him for a while. Maybe he would move into a luxury hotel for a time. He had enough goddamn money.

The timer next to the No Smoking sign showed six minutes to burn. There was something nagging at the back of Marlowe's mind, something more than the natural trepidation at the coming reentry. Indeed, Marlowe had been in space for so long that his fear of flying had become almost vestigial. It appeared to be true that given enough time one could get used to anything. As far as he could tell, what he was feeling was a sense of incompleteness. He knew the adventure was over. The fat lady had definitely sung. Right up until he had stepped into the umbilical lead-in to the shuttle, there had been the sneaking fear that he would be whisked off to Jupiter, or something equally absurd, and a new chapter in the drama would begin. Now that he was actually strapped in, though, he knew that he was going back to his old life and his old ways. He should have been pleased, but a brand-new doubt had attached itself to him. Maybe his old ways wouldn't make it anymore. Would it even be possible to go back to playacting after such an overdose of reality?

The captain's voice came over the intercom. "Umbilical ready to detach. Attendants, arm and seal the port, please."

These new doubts, however, weren't the whole of it. The incompleteness was that he knew so little of what had really happened over the last few weeks, the real nature of the forces that had dragged him across the country and finally into space. He had the big picture—or, at least, he thought that he did. But the details remained hidden in the labyrinth of corporate conspiracy. What irked him most was that he would probably never know who had hired him in the first place. He didn't even know who had sent the phony Veronica Stavers to recruit him as a pawn in the game. Somehow it would have been comforting to know who was responsible for what he had been through. Unfortunately, nobody cared too much about the comfort of pawns.

"We are detaching from the installation. There will be a certain amount of vibration."

The timer read two minutes to burn. The shuttle was dropping away from the installation. Marlowe was pushed down in the contour berth as the thrusters cut in. They were no longer in orbit. Within minutes they would hit the atmosphere. The engineer from the ore carrier was still muttering about aliens. The shuttle started to vibrate, and Marlowe got a good grip of the seat arms.

ABOUT THE AUTHOR

Mick Farren was born in Cheltenham, England, on September 3, 1944, was educated at St. Martin's School of Art, and hasn't held a steady job since the mid-sixties. Instead he has divided his time between science fiction, popular music, and media criticism. During the late sixties and early seventies he was the lead singer with the notorious Deviants, who have frequently been cited as one of the major precursors of punk rock. He has published a number of novels both in Britain and the USA, as well as nonfiction works on rock music and pop culture. In addition, he has published comic books and also worked on TV and movie scripts. In 1980, lured by the city's essential craziness, he moved from London to New York and currently lives in lower Manhattan where he continues to write fiction, contribute to a wide range of magazines, and participate in various musical projects.